A CENTURY IN PHOTOGRAPHS

Published jointly by
Shropshire Federation of Women's Institutes
and Countryside Books

COUNTRYSIDE BOOKS
3 Catherine Road
Newbury, Berkshire

ISBN 1 85306 477 7

FRONT COVER PHOTOGRAPH OF THE GIRL GUIDES CAR WASH AT
HEMMINGS GARAGE, BISHOP'S CASTLE
SUPPLIED BY LUCY HEMMINGS VIA JANET PRESHOUS, LYDHAM WI

BACK COVER PHOTOGRAPH SHOWING SHREWSBURY IN FLOOD C1900
SUPPLIED BY MARY EVANS, ST GILES WI

PHOTOGRAPH ON PAGE 1 OF HAYMAKING AT WESTBURY
SUPPLIED BY BERYL HOLLINGWORTH, WESTBURY WI

Designed by Graham Whiteman

Produced through MRM Associates Ltd., Reading

Printed by Woolnough Bookbinding Ltd., Irthlingborough

CONTENTS

Kate Smith out with her bicycle near Halfpenny Green, on the south-east Shropshire border.

(Eileen Roberts - Withington WI)

FOREWORD

I am delighted that our members have created this lovely record of life in Shropshire over the last century. This is the third book produced in partnership with Countryside Books, joining the very successful *Within Living Memory* and *Shropshire Village Book*.

A century seems a long time but it represents just a couple of lifetimes. We, who now stand on the threshold of the new Millennium, will have known many people who saw the beginning of this century – in many cases our own grandparents. The changes that time has brought are phenomenal – from horse and cart to two-car families; from pen and ink to the computer age; and, in between, the dark years of two World Wars.

I do hope you enjoy seeing the changes evolve through the chapters of this book. It is also a record of how lovely our county of Shropshire is and how fortunate we are to live here.

Margaret Leverton
Federation Chairman

ACKNOWLEDGEMENTS

We would like to thank everyone who has given so much time and effort in the preparation of this book. Most of all, many thanks to all those WI members who have sent their photographs in order that this book might be produced. Thank you also for your patience.

Much appreciation goes to Countryside Books for their hard work in pulling all the details together.

We do hope you enjoy reading the book.

Sue Johnson
Federation Secretary

INTO THE 20TH CENTURY

(1900 – 1919)

At the turn of the century Queen Victoria was still on the throne and Shropshire was a county of small, often isolated, villages and a few bustling market and industrial towns.

Roads were often no more than rough tracks, muddy in winter and dusty in summer. The motor car was a rarity and horse-drawn vehicles were still the principal means of transport. The fastest thing on the road was the bicycle, which caused similar alarm among parents of young children as do the cars of today.

But progress moved at an alarming rate and by the time of the First World War the local papers carried advertisements for cars – a Studebaker was for sale by M. Davies Ltd of Shrewsbury at £295. How much this must have seemed to the average worker whose annual wage was probably one-tenth of that amount!

What probably attracted more attention amongst the rural community were advertisements for and local demonstrations of tractors costing slightly less at £285 – 'the cost of three good horses, making it possible to plough ten acres a day rather than one for the cost of 1s 8d for paraffin.'

There was electricity but it was only applied to industry on a small scale. In the home families relied on candles or oil lamps, or fragile gas lights. Water came from the well or the pump, often shared with other cottages, or sometimes straight from the stream. It would be many decades before indoor plumbing and running water replaced the earth closet and bucket in every home.

Children were taught in all-age schools, leaving as soon as they could and starting work the next day – the boys on the land or in factories, mines or quarries, while the girls might look for farmwork or go into service. Society was still very structured and the 'big house' and the local church or chapel exerted great influence.

The war in 1914 brought hardship to every home and heartbreak for many. Shropshire's town and village war memorials bear witness to the thousands of local men who went away to the war and never returned. Nothing could ever be quite the same again.

The war brought calls for women to join the Women's National Land Service Corps. A national organiser came to Shropshire to sell the idea. She said women found 'pigsty cleaning preferable to drawing room dusting'. Perhaps she was a little too innocent for country tastes because she went on to say that 'farmers couldn't wait to get hold of them', which naturally brought the house down.

Alfred and Edith Williams and family at Rye Bank Farm, Wem, 1903.
(June Parry – Longden WI)

1900 – 1919

Mr Randles working on the buddles at Snailbeach 1915. Mining had ceased in 1911 but work continued in a limited way under the Halvans Company until the 1950s extracting lead, barytes and fluorspar from the waste at a place called the buddles. (Emily Griffiths – Snailbeach WI)

Oswestry cattle market in 1916, a social occasion for farmers as well as an essential part of rural life. (Ronald Hartshorne)

A view of the Stiperstones at the turn of the century, showing the school, inn and Primitive Methodist chapel nestling at the base of the Oak Hill, with the Central Stores and the white dumps of Snailbeach lead mines in the distance. (Emily Griffiths – Snailbeach WI)

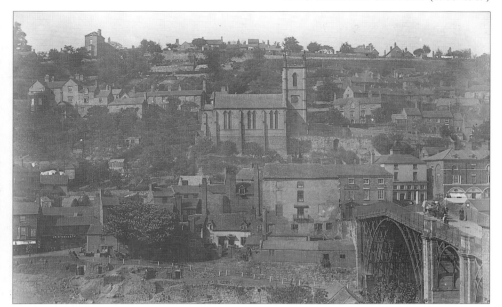

Above Ironbridge in 1902
with the famous bridge and
the church beyond, a view
now obscured by trees. This
little working class town is
today the centre of a
thriving tourist industry.
(Margaret Beddoes –
Brockton WI)

Below Coalport Tollhouse,
on the Madeley Turnpike,
in 1902. A large sign on
the house wall lists the tolls,
which were collected as late
as 1909.
(Margaret Beddoes –
Brockton WI)

In October 1907 the mail train from Scotland failed to slow as it approached Shrewsbury Station and went into a tight bend at about 60 miles per hour. The train overturned and 15 people were killed. The cause of the disaster remains a mystery.
(Ronald Hartshorne)

An affectionate look at 'our local express', on the Bishops Castle to Craven Arms line in 1907. Rural lines, no matter how slow, came to be an integral part of country life.
(Ronald Hartshorne)

OUR LOCAL EXPRESS
P.T.O.   BISHOP'S CASTLE TO CRAVEN ARMS.

Above Knowbury Road at the turn of the century was typical of many village roads – today the road is tarmacked, there is no footpath, and the school in front of the church is a private house.
(Pam Cole – Ludlow WI)

Below In 1906 an escaped captive balloon from Shrewsbury landed at Knightley, near Newport. It illustrates the lively – and immediate – trade in postcards of local events. The sender says it was bought 'from the stout man and he will bring another one tomorrow for Auntie Florrie!'
(Mary Croxton – Lilleshall WI)

ESCAPED CAPTIVE BALLOON FROM SHREWSBURY, 1906
LANDED WITH PASSENGERS AT KNIGHTLEY
NEAR NEWPORT
OSBOURNE, PHOTO
WOODSEAVES NEWPORT, SALOP
SALOP

11

Darby's boot and shoe repair shop with William Darby in the centre. This was on the Shrewsbury side of the Cock Inn, now Rectory Gardens, Hanwood, in 1915. Boots and shoes required frequent mending and were often handed down within families till they could be worn no more. Small tradesmen were in every village, providing for the immediate needs of local people. It was still possible to meet people who had never travelled beyond their native parish, even for shopping in the nearest market town.
(Hilda Morgan – Lea Cross WI)

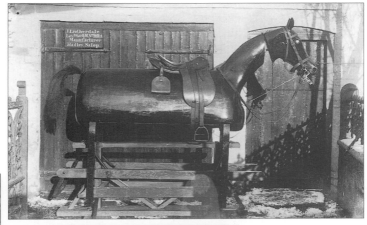

Above This full size rocking horse must have given customers at J. Leatherdale's of Hadley a good impression of the comfort – or otherwise – of their new saddle before they tried it on the real thing. Sadly there is today no trace of the saddleworks.
(Mary Croxton – Lilleshall WI)

Transport had changed little since Victorian days for many families and it was still more common to see people out for a spin in a pony and trap than a motor car! Wonderful on warm sunny days, but so often wet and cold with only a waterproof rug over the knees for comfort.
(Barbara Pollard – Worthen WI)

*A display of poultry outside
No 1 Mardol, Shrewsbury.
Such displays were
common outside the better
quality butcher's shop.
Hygiene left a lot to be
desired, the meat hanging
without protection from
flies and dust.*
(Age Concern, Shropshire)

Below *Arthur Greenhous
and Son's shop in Bishops
Castle – an ironmongery
emporium.*
(Janet Preshous – Lydham, More and Snead WI)

Workers at Pontesbury Quarries c1910. There was a number of roadstone quarries in the area, and a neighbouring one at Callow Hill is still working today.
(Emily Griffiths – Snailbeach WI)

Outside the Royal Insurance Company Fire Brigade headquarters in Shrewsbury. Insurance companies had their own fire brigades. A subscriber would have a cast iron plate affixed to his house or shop wall indicating which company had responsibility and should be summoned if fire broke out. Many can still be seen on buildings in the town.
(Age Concern, Shropshire)

INTO THE 20TH CENTURY (1900–1919)

Men at the iron foundry at Welsh Bridge. The Atlas Foundry, owned by the Davies family, is still working on the same site today.
(Age Concern, Shropshire)

A dairy class in north Shropshire c1910, probably near Whitchurch. Dairying was traditionally a woman's responsibility. The piece of equipment on the left is a butter worker – a roller being used to squeeze out the buttermilk.
(Hilda Morgan – Lea Cross WI)

Sheep shearing at High Onn 1916 using a hand-cranked shearing machine.
(Kath Lewis – Pitchcroft and Church Aston WI)

The Sheedy family haymaking at Kempton. All the family, young and old, came out into the fields at this busy time of the year, cutting and then raking the hay into mounds which would be turned regularly. The sweet scent of cut hay was one of the pleasures of summertime.
(Valerie Sheedy – Withington WI)

INTO THE 20TH CENTURY (1900–1919)

Twins Mary (Mollie) Taylor and Muriel Corden Smith were born at the end of the 1800s. Mollie died in 1944 and Muriel in 1984. Pushing the pram is their eldest sister Margaret, outside the family home at Brockton Hall, near Shifnal.
(Margaret Beddoes – Brockton WI)

At the rear of a house in Mill Lane, Hadnall in 1906. The baby in the pram is now aged 91 and was a founder member of Hadnall WI. The various barrels and tubs would be needed on washday for the processes of washing, rinsing, blueing, wringing and mangling – a day of drudgery that came round only too quickly every week.
(Ivy Bebb – Hadnall WI)

Inside an old house in Shrewsbury at the turn of the century. The range was often the heart of the house, providing heat and a means of cooking and boiling water. There would have been no other source of warmth in the house, so that a place by the fire in the evening was a great comfort on cold days. Many families were large and lived in very cramped conditions, children sleeping two or more to a bed.
(Age Concern, Shropshire)

Maypole dancing at Knighton on Teme school in 1908. Most schools erected maypoles for the children to dance around, often as an entertainment for parents and villagers. The often very intricate dances were diligently learned and performed. The month of May also brought Empire Day, when schoolchildren were given a half day's holiday.
(Ronald Hartshorne)

The May Queen, Norah Elliott, at Upton Magna in 1904. Another popular May Day custom, every year a young girl was elected Queen by her fellows.
(Ronald Hartshorne)

St Lawrence's School, Lower Galdeford, Ludlow. The leaving age had been raised to 12 in 1899, except for children who worked on the land and who were often working as adults when barely 10 or 11 years old. Many children left school as soon as they were able to, their families needing their earnings, and very few went on to secondary education – which in any case had to be paid for unless you were lucky enough to qualify for a grant.
(Joan Collings – Hayton WI)

Pupils at Stapleton school 1912. They had apparently just been told of the sinking of the Titanic *and it had made a deep impression on them – perhaps the cause of their serious expressions.* (Hilda Morgan – Lea Cross WI)

Beautifully dressed for a tea party at the former Primitive Methodist chapel at The Grove, Minsterley c1900. This is now a private house. (Emily Griffiths – Snailbeach WI)

Wentnor, Worthen and Stiperstones schools were Church of England and a Church Army van visited the area at times.
(Emily Griffiths – Snailbeach WI)

The Oddfellows Wakes Walk at Cheswardine in 1908. Wakes Week was the first week in July and each day a different organisation held a 'walk' followed by games. The custom ended in the late 1920s.
(Vera Ward – Cheswardine WI)

Snailbeach White Stars footballers 1910. Most villages had their own teams and local matches were keenly contested.
(Emily Griffiths – Snailbeach WI)

Clun Show procession in 1910. Local fairs and fetes were often the high spot of the year, attracting spectators from all the villages around. Members of the family who had moved away from the village to find work would often make a point of coming home for the day.
(Ronald Hartshorne)

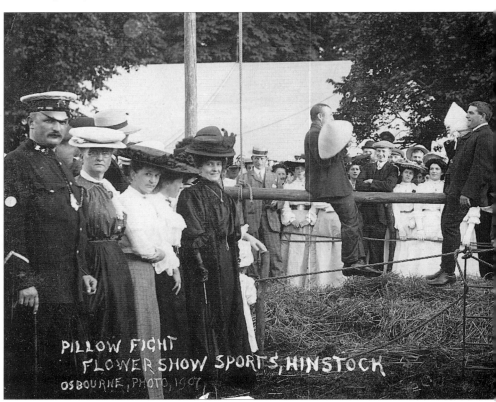

These gentlemen seem very well dressed for taking part in the pillow fight at Hinstock Flower Show in 1907. Such undignified games delighted the spectators. Flower shows had become very popular during Victorian times and continued to thrive, combining competition with entertainment.
(Joan Collings – Hayton WI)

Castle Street, Shrewsbury decorated for the Coronation celebrations in 1911. Sports, games, bonfires, dances and parish teas were on the programme all over the county. George V, the present Queen's grandfather, was to prove a quieter, more respectable king after the rather scandalous reign of King Edward VII. His Silver Jubilee in 1935 would be just as popular a cause for celebration.
(Ronald Hartshorne)

The stables at the Army remount depot at The Firs, Astley. The depot broke and trained horses for the Army – essential as war loomed in 1914. Local children were often frightened by the partly-broken horses out on the country lanes, not yet completely under control.
(Mary Evans – St Giles WI)

During the First World War an Army camp and hospital
was built at Prees Heath. This refreshment canteen was the
first to be set up by Mr E.C. Pointon of Whitchurch who
already had a small business in the town. It is believed to
have provided food and drink for the workmen who were
building the camp. Prees Heath was again built on during
the Second World War, firstly to provide a prisoner of war
camp for Italians who worked on local farms. Later it
became RAF Tilstock. The only reminders of its wartime
past today are the hangars, which have fulfilled many uses
including as grain stores during the time of the 'grain
mountain', and the old control tower.
(Brenda Evans – Tilstock WI)

The camp at Prees Heath not only provided accommodation and training for troops waiting to go overseas, but also entertainment. The Palace Theatre was used by the soldiers and by locals. The theatre later became a cafe and was destroyed by fire in 1940.
(Brenda Evans – Tilstock WI)

Victor Kidd, Ernest Normansell and other soldiers were sent out to farmers by the Army under a scheme to provide help with the harvest. It was compulsory to billet the soldiers posted to you and these men, at Broome, near Clun, had been all over Shropshire helping on the farms.
(Dorothy Rudd – Hopesay WI)

29

BETWEEN THE WARS

(1920 – 1938)

These were hard decades for many people. The 1920s saw a great deal of slum clearance in Shropshire, but workhouses were still in operation and a thin line separated those in work and those on the dole.

In the farming world there was a general welcome for the new national milk scheme which guaranteed a market for the producer. There was concern about imports of subsidised meat from Germany. Agricultural wages were set by the Shropshire Committee in 1925 at 31s 6d for a 54 hour week.

Crime seemed more innocent but the law a little more harsh. Pedlar John Taylor was sent to prison for 14 days in 1925 for using bad language, while the magistrates at Oswestry that same week heard that Ernest Jones was caught riding his bicycle with his hands in his pockets. He had to dig deep in those pockets to pay his ten shilling fine plus costs.

Town carnivals were very popular and in the 1920s the Shrewsbury Chamber of Commerce suggested a pageant to advertise the town and attract tourists.

Not only did the press print a good many details of local people, but they were expected to! A 1929 report of the wedding of the son of Viscount Bridgeman took a full three and a half columns of the local paper. It listed the guests at the wedding and all the gifts the happy couple received and from whom – from furniture and silverware down to doilies.

The Shropshire Federation of Women's Institutes had been launched in 1919 and one of its first chairmen, Miss Edith Ward, referred to the spirit of co-operation and the 'awakening civic sense which is stirring in the souls of countrywomen'. She contrasted the dreariness of the life of village women in former times with the opportunities now opened up to them.

Women had got the vote, though those under 30 had to wait until 1928 for the privilege. Employment opportunities were still limited, few women working after they were married.

It was the age of the small tradesman and the whistling errand boy, of the village and corner shop. Horse and cart began to give way to motorised van but orders were still called for every week at the door.

The waterworks at Shelton were inaugurated on 4th July 1935 costing over £100,000. Water had been chlorinated since 1909 – one of the first towns to introduce it.

The crystal set and then the wireless kept us entertained, while the cinema took

Thomas Price stooking wheat at Sundorne Grove Farm in 1930.
(Denise Morris – Sundorne WI)

1920 – 1938

its own hold on our lives with silent films at first and then increasingly sophisticated 'talkies'.

Clothes became lighter and more comfortable, though hats were still essential outdoor wear. Fewer children were sewn into their underclothes for the winter! Women's fashions mirrored their increasing independence and activity outside the home.

Village schools had changed little since Victorian days, but the leaving age was raised to 14. Proposals to raise it yet again to 15 were discussed by the County Council's Education Committee in the late 1920s. 'The cost will undoubtedly frighten the Council and appal the ratepayers, but if the nation requires it, it will have to be faced,' said a councillor at the time. It did not have to be faced until 1947. Once again war came and disrupted our lives.

Cars queuing for the new bypass in Shrewsbury 1936. A flurry of housing development followed the building of the road.
(Age Concern, Shropshire)

31

BETWEEN THE WARS (1920-1938)

The first Midland Red bus to run on the Shrewsbury-Hanwood-Pontesbury-Minsterley route, on a trial run on a Sunday morning in the 1920s. The man on the right was the Hanwood chapel Sunday school superintendent. Sadly, the Midland Red no longer runs this route.
(Hilda Morgan – Lea Cross WI)

Mr and Miss Owen at Knockin in the 1930s. Some people preferred real horse-power to the increasingly intrusive motor car. Country roads were often still rather rough and ready, more suited to an older style of travel.
(Olwen Owen – Knockin WI)

Ann Reynolds, a school teacher at the primary school in Church Stretton, poses proudly with her first car in 1929. Cars were becoming more affordable. The difference 20 years had made in women's fashions and outlook was astounding!
(Dulcie Henderson – Rushbury & Cardington WI)

Salop County Council workers in the late 1920s. Motorised traffic was demanding better road surfaces. The days when a stonebreaker could be seen painstakingly reducing rocks to small stones to fill holes was almost over!
(Joan Collings – Hayton & District WI)

Below An aeroplane came down in fields at Cherrington in 1936 when it ran out of fuel. Planes were a rare sight around here and the local schoolboys were soon on hand.
(Vera Chadwick – Tibberton WI)

On many farms horses were still providing the power – here at Bury Farm, Hawkestone in the 1920s.
(June Parry – Longden WI)

And turning the hay was still a family affair at East Wall Farm. The lady in the hat was Sarah Henderson, whose parents migrated from Scotland in the 1870s. The Hendersons farm here today, now into the fifth generation.
(Dulcie Henderson – Rushbury & Cardington WI)

A working horse ready for a show in the Hanwood area c1930. Holding the horse is Charlie Andrews who lived at Cruckmeole.
(Arthur Evans, via Lea Cross WI)

Top Reg Lippett with the 'Atora Suet' wagon, bringing the oxen (Sinbad and Sailor) to be shod at the forge, Bromfield, in the 1920s. This is today the A49 road.
(Barbara Tomkins – Bromfield WI)

Above Jim Lomas and Edgar Evans at Bostock Hall crossroads, Whixall c1938. The old farmhouse was pulled down in 1980.
(Jean Matthews – Prees WI)

BETWEEN THE WARS (1920-1938)

Tom Houlding's parents farmed at Lacon Farm near Prees, in the far north of the county, in the 1920s. (June Parry – Longden WI)

The Adams family, cheesemakers at Minsterley creamery in the late 1920s. (Thea Beddoes – St Giles WI)

THEN & NOW
Bridgnorth – the view from the Castle Walk and as it is now. Very little seems to have changed except for the traffic! The High Towns and Low Towns are linked by a funicular railway which still runs today, taking passengers up the steep incline. (SFWI)

Cruckmeole Colliery in the 1920s. It became part of the Hanwood and Moat Hall Company. The bridge parapet in the centre background still shows rope marks from the cable-hauled tramway incline. (Barbara Wellings – Lea Cross WI)

Unveiling the War Memorial, Loppington, Nr. Wem.

Above *Unveiling the war memorial at Loppington.
Similar ceremonies took place all over the county in the
1920s. Armistice Day was strictly observed, life coming to a
silent halt for two minutes every 11th November.*
(June Parry – Longden WI)

Below *Inside a ward at the Ellesmere Red Cross Hospital.
The Red Cross branch had been founded in 1911. It
became a cottage hospital and is now a community
nursing home.*
(Anne Hayes – Loppington WI)

Washday at the blacksmith's shop, Bromfield! The heavy mangle stands ready to squeeze out the water. At least it was sunny – rainy days made washday a miserable time of steamy condensation and wet washing hung indoors.
(Barbara Tomkins – Bromfield WI)

The village shop in Hanwood in the 1930s. This wooden lock-up shop was built in the early 1900s and demolished in the 1970s. A wide variety of goods was offered for sale, ranging from patent medicines to bicycles.
(Hilda Morgan – Lea Cross WI)

The post office in Post Office Lane, Whixall, was run by Mr and Mrs Moore in 1908. Taken over in the 1920s by Mr and Mrs Harry Law, and then by Miss Winnie Preston in 1949, it finally closed in 1973 and business was transferred to Waterloo post office.
(Helen Phillips – Clive & Grinshill WI)

'Gran and Grandad Smith'
drawing water from a
shared well at their cottage
near Halfpenny Green. It
would be some time before
mains water reached every
part of the county. When a
large quantity of water was
needed, especially on
washday, it was hard work
getting up the full buckets.
(Eileen Roberts –
Withington & District WI)

Below *Taking the girls out*
for a punt on the river was
a popular pastime in the
1920s!
(Jean Bebb- High Ercall
WI)

Atcham Women's Institute on an outing – and expecting all types of weather judging by the clothes!
(Robert Evason WI)

Tibberton women's cricket team formed in 1929. They played on the village pitch and changed in the cowshed. Refreshments were served from a wheelbarrow!
(Joyce Wilton – Tibberton WI)

BETWEEN THE WARS (1920-1938)

The Bishops Castle mixed hockey team in the 1923-24 season. The sport flourished locally in the 1920s.
(Mrs Bob Jones – Lydham, More & Snead WI)

Below *The Ludlow Hunt meet at the church at Bromfield in the 1920s. Many came out to follow the hunt on foot.*
(Barbara Tomkins – Bromfield WI)

William Teague, retired blacksmith, wheelwright and undertaker, starting the races at Bromfield Show.
(Barbara Tomkins – Bromfield WI)

The Elite Dance Band formed in 1925 by Bill Thomas, the saxophonist. Based in Shrewsbury, they played all over the county at balls, dances and parties. Three were carpenters during the day, working from 6am. They split up in 1933.
(Thelma Costley – Pulverbatch WI)

43

Below *Youngsters of East Hamlet, Ludlow celebrating the*
1937 Coronation of King George VI. This was the second
royal occasion, 1935 seeing George V's Silver Jubilee.
(Mary Hall – Diddlebury WI)

Left *Ludlow Council School Group I in 1931. The years between the wars were a time of great freedom for children, something which later generations would sadly not experience.* (Joan Collings – Hayton WI)

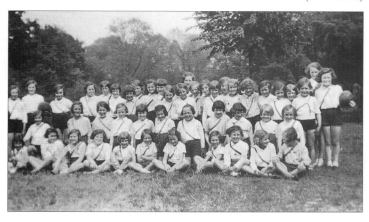

Below *The Rose Queen ceremony for the girls of Hook-a-Gate school in 1935 at Annscroft Church Fete.* (Hilda Morgan – Lea Cross WI)

Above *Every July the Shrewsbury Schools held matches on the Gay Meadow. This was the year the Lancastrian School won the cup in the 1930s.* (Muriel Painter – Shawbury WI)

45

The Second World War

(1939 – 1945)

On Sunday morning, 3rd September 1939, Prime Minister Chamberlain announced that we were at war with Germany. For many months afterwards we went through the 'phoney war', waiting for an onslaught that never came. Then the dark days of Dunkirk and the Battle of Britain brought the reality of modern warfare home to us all.

The *Shrewsbury Chronicle* was honoured to be among the first six newspapers invited to send correspondents to the Front, with the aim of bringing the public more closely in touch with the activities of the local regiments overseas.

Shrewsbury prison began releasing prisoners on short term sentences in 1939 to make way for more prisoners moved out from the larger towns and cities. Church Stretton UDC agreed to sterilise the water supply at a cost of £349 15s because of the possibility of water being contaminated during wartime.

The war years changed many things. There were complaints of girls 'apeing men in smoking, drinking and wearing manly garments'. All this, it was said, would ruin their health and make them unattractive to a man who wanted a wife. Yet women were needed in all parts of industry and agriculture to replace men called up for the services, and many more joined up themselves as the war dragged on.

Rationing brought about a great deal of ingenuity with recipes and food production. Shropshire farmers were experimenting in the production of bacon from mutton. MPs had tried it in the dining rooms of the Houses of Parliament and declared it delicious. However, no one quite knew what to call it – should it be macon or button? An intriguing recipe for vegetarian duck was very disappointing – it turned out to be marrow with sage and onion stuffing.

The blackout brought its own problems. One Shrewsbury housewife called for the door handles of shops to be painted white so they could be spotted in the gloom. Apart from accidents on the roads, there were collisions between people on the pavements and pedestrians were advised to keep to the left.

The county was host to very many evacuees, with horror stories on both sides. Some host families complained of the dirtiness of their guests, others that the amount given to them for each evacuee was not enough: '8s 6d may be enough to feed a young girl but certainly would not meet the needs of a strong lad of 15'. But others were touched by the sight of silent trainloads of bewildered children arriving from Liverpool.

In February 1942 a Whitley bomber towing a glider on a practice mission crashed into the Stiperstones. The six occupants of the plane were killed but the pilot

Annie Powell was a chimney sweep in the Wistanstow area during the war.
(Bernard Evans, via Lea Cross WI)

1939 – 1945

managed to release the glider which landed safely.

Shropshire was the recipient of many German bombs jettisoned after bombing missions elsewhere, like the land mine that fell at Nobold. One night a string of incendiary flares ('Molotov breadbaskets') were dropped along the Stiperstones and beyond. The real target was a number of Home Office explosives stores hidden in woods alongside the A49 from Craven Arms to Ludlow. Lord Haw Haw (who had Shropshire connections being part of the Joyce of Whitchurch clockmaker family) reported that the German raid had been successful but in fact the only damage was a burnt out hay rick.

Country ways were still to the fore in this new age. In Craven Arms a farmer, Mr Bywater, still practised the skill of bone setting, passed down through his family. He never advertised but had a steady stream of people from all backgrounds coming to his door.

A Good Neighbour Scheme started towards the end of the war by the WVS to collect household equipment to send to Hackney bomb victims met with a wonderful response. The articles were gratefully received but it did prove difficult to find a home for a splendid pair of stag's antlers!

The porter, stationmaster, clerk, signalman and driver at Berrington station on the Great Western Railway line in July 1944. The RAF station at Atcham, taken over by the Americans, created a lot of traffic. (Eileen Owen – Clive & Grinshill WI)

THE SECOND WORLD WAR (1939-1945)

Clive and Grinshill Home Guard c1940. The Home Guard comprised men from the two villages under the direction of Mr Vaughan who was the estate agent at Sansaw. They took part in manoeuvres on Grinshill Hill and were all issued with rifles or sten guns. Nights were spent on guard against possible parachute invasion or bombing raids, usually after a hard day at their own work.
(Clive & Grinshill WI)

The Wellington Auxiliary Fire Service crew on standby during the war – the young boy in overalls was their messenger. Like the members of the Home Guard, great pride was taken by these men in their service on the Home Front.
(Mary Croxton – Lilleshall WI)

Above Mary Corfield served in the WAAFs during the war. She is pictured about to set off from Monkmoor Main Unit to Whitehall to deliver a load of parachutes.
(Mary Corfield – Sundorne WI)

The Shrewsbury Auxiliary Fire Service with some of the cups they won at inter-service competitions during the war.
(Rachel Walton – Bicton & Oxon WI)

Special Constables at Wistanstow Village Hall, 1942. A number came from the Grove, Craven Arms, including the butler, head gardener and several under gardeners. Another was a stonemason and the Sergeant was the local blacksmith. Several of them were members of the Wistanstow Brass Band. (Bernard Evans, via Lea Cross WI)

Harvesting the corn at Bromlow Hall, Minsterley in the 1940s. As food supplies became scarcer farmers were urged to lay down more land to arable, which did not go down well with dairy farmers. (Thea Beddoes – St Giles WI)

Joan Baxter and Kathleen were land girls working at Charlton Farm, near Wellington in 1943. The Women's Land Army recruited girls from all walks of life to take the place on the land of men called up into the armed forces.
(Margaret Beddoes – Brockton WI)

Mrs Maura Gough served in the Women's Timber Corps (a second

Items collected for a Living History Exhibition in 1994, recalling the work of the Women's Timber Corps. Like the land girls they took on men's work, felling timber and clearing ground. The work was physically very hard but great friendships were formed which have stood the test of time.
(Janet Preshous – Lydham, More & Snead WI)

Ministry of Food staff in the grounds of Swan Hill Court, Shrewsbury 1941. The house had been requisitioned for the purpose, staff dealing with ration books and food emergencies.
(Muriel Painter – Shawbury WI)

Above left

Many large houses were requisitioned, or volunteered by their owners, for use in the war effort. Hodnet Hall was used as an emergency hospital during the war. It is the home of Algernon Heber-Percy, the Lord Lieutenant of the County and today its gardens are open to the public.
(Mary Corfield – Sundorne WI)

Above right

Olwen and Edith Davies were nurses there in 1943 and a reunion was held in 1985.
(Olwen Owen – Knockin WI)

Pontesbury Junior Girls' Club with teachers and evacuees at a garden fete in the Deanery Garden, Pontesbury, in aid of the Red Cross in June 1943. Despite some difficulties, great efforts were made to make evacuees feel wanted and at home during their enforced stay in the country.
(Thea Beddoes – St Giles WI)

Members of Ellesmere Women's Institute at a fruit preserving session during the war. Everyone was exhorted to 'dig for victory' and to waste nothing, and the summer months were a continuous round of picking, jamming, pickling, bottling and drying, strictly supervised through the WI. The results were eagerly bought by hungry customers.
(Ellesmere WI)

George Napp was gamekeeper on the Aqualate Estate, Newport, a great character who also made radio broadcasts. The labrador was an evacuee – his London owner had sent him to Shropshire for safety!
(Edna Peacock – Pitchcroft & Church Aston WI)

Left Jam making at Upton Magna 1941. Gwynedd LLoyd, later President of the Shropshire Federation, was responsible for inspecting jam production throughout Shropshire and on one visit found just one member frantically trying to cope, rushing from pan to pan stirring furiously. She explained, 'There's rather a good funeral in the village and all the others have gone to it.'
(Kath Neville – Withington & District WI)

Above This American GI 'borrowed' toddlers Peter and Michael one day in Shrewsbury, outside the Raven Hotel. He wanted his picture taken to send home to his wife saying, 'Honey, look what I've produced in England....twins!' We hope she had a sense of humour!
(Esme Morris – Nobold WI)

The Victory party held at St George's School, Frankwell, Shrewsbury in 1945. The parish hall had been used before that to house Italian prisoners of war.
(Kath Buckley – Belvidere WI)

THE POST-WAR YEARS

(1946 – 1959)

The ending of the war brought a feeling of change and a new beginning, despite the hardships that continued for so many years. The editorial writer of the *Shrewsbury Chronicle* reflected on the changes of the first half of the century. 'We do not boast the jingoism of 1901 and our military prowess as we did then. Our new more rational outlook on national defence is one of stern resolution and a willingness to sink sectional differences in the interest of the nation.' The Cold War had already begun.

Rationing went on and bread did not come off ration until 1948. Children were delighted when at last they could buy as many sweets as they liked in 1953. Coal stayed on ration until 1958!

But brighter changes were coming to the county. In 1949 television arrived with the opening of the Sutton Coldfield transmitter. Three hundred television sets were sold in Shrewsbury, with fewer in the market towns. Many people saw their first television programme on Coronation Day 1953, when the events in London were broadcast live for the very first time.

The war had brought many more divorces, though a Marriage Guidance Council speaker at a meeting in Shrewsbury thought that the peak had been reached. He felt that difficulties on the physical side of married life were to blame for up to 90 per cent of marriage breakdowns.

There were demographic changes too. In 1947 women outnumbered men by two to one in England and Wales – there was a popular comic song *Three Women To Every Man*. The number of people over 65 rose and under-15s fell. The 'baby boom' was yet to come. But the signs were there of a changing emphasis on youth – the 'teenager' was born and music and fashions catered for the first time for this young audience.

Women wanted modern appliances to make their lives easier and took prospective parliamentary candidates to task at a Shrewsbury meeting because vacuum cleaners, refrigerators and washing machines were subject to purchase tax as 'luxuries'. The Labour candidate won himself few votes by saying that they most certainly were luxuries, and if the tax wasn't paid on them it would have to be paid on something else!

The county worried about a lack of water. Many people were still using pumps, and pumping was becoming harder and harder. Local people felt the introduction of the mains system was taking more than their fair share of water to city folk.

There was a boom in house building

Bringing in the cows for milking at Bromfield in the late 1940s.
(Barbara Tomkins – Bromfield WI)

and in the four years after the end of the war over 3,000 houses were completed in Shropshire, most local authority owned. Hundreds of temporary houses and 550 privately built still did not solve the housing shortage and squatting was a real problem, particularly in the now empty army camps dotted around the county.

In 1949 a private member's bill came before Parliament to ban fox-hunting. The same year the film *Gone to Earth* starring Jennifer Jones was made at various sites around south Shropshire, based on the book by local author Mary Webb and one of the first films to be made in Technicolour.

Bob-a-Job Weeks during the Fifties found boys undertaking all sorts of tasks! Here, Cubs from the 2nd Wellington Pack give a wash and brush up to the new arrivals at Wheeler's pet shop in Wellington.
(Mary Croxton – Lilleshall WI)

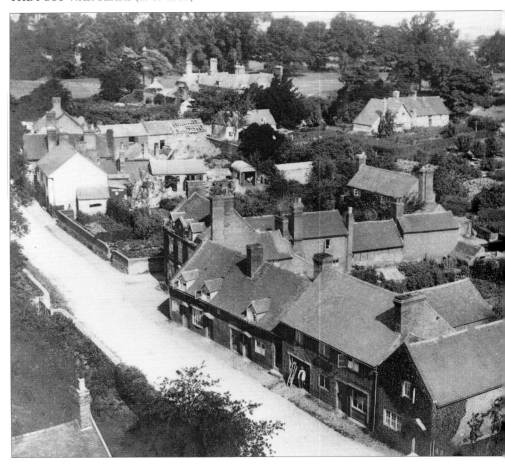

Cleaning out Whittington pond in 1946. It is actually part of the old moat around Whittington Castle, and needs clearing of green algae and moss every few years.
(Margaret Taylor – West Felton WI)

THEN & NOW
Looking down over the village of Condover from the church
tower in 1900 and a view along the road towards the
church in 1959. It is still a very peaceful scene, with few
changes. Fewer inhabitants were now tied to the land and
the big estates than at the beginning of the century.
(Anne Muir – Condover WI)

Knockin in the late 1940s,
with bicycles and horse-
power still very much in
evidence.
(Olwen Owen – Knockin
WI)

Ludlow in the late 1950s. Cars had begun to dominate the streets, the beginning of a problem that has faced all towns over the last half of the century. However, little else has changed in this lovely old town.
(Beryl Hollingworth – Westbury WI)

THEN & NOW
Tong Castle in 1904 was an imposing and substantial great house. After the First World War it was left empty and fell into disrepair. In 1954 an army explosives team was called in to demolish it and the land was then left to grow wild.
(Mary Croxton – Lilleshall WI)

Above Linotype machine operators at the Wellington Journal and Shrewsbury News in 1958. These machines produced lead slugs of type, one column wide, which were set up as news pages. In 1965 the paper was taken over and the works moved to Ketley where a new web-offset process was installed. Now that has been outmoded by the fully computerised system used today. (Mary Croxton – Lilleshall WI)

John Owen of Lane End Forge shoeing a horse – the car came in handy as a hitching post. John Owen came to the forge as an apprentice but by 1960 was himself the blacksmith with two apprentices. Though the days of the working horse were gone, there were still many riding horses to keep blacksmiths busy after the war.
(Betty Pearce – West Felton WI)

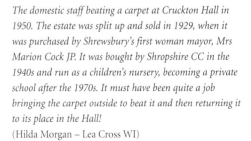

The domestic staff beating a carpet at Cruckton Hall in 1950. The estate was split up and sold in 1929, when it was purchased by Shrewsbury's first woman mayor, Mrs Marion Cock JP. It was bought by Shropshire CC in the 1940s and run as a children's nursery, becoming a private school after the 1970s. It must have been quite a job bringing the carpet outside to beat it and then returning it to its place in the Hall!
(Hilda Morgan – Lea Cross WI)

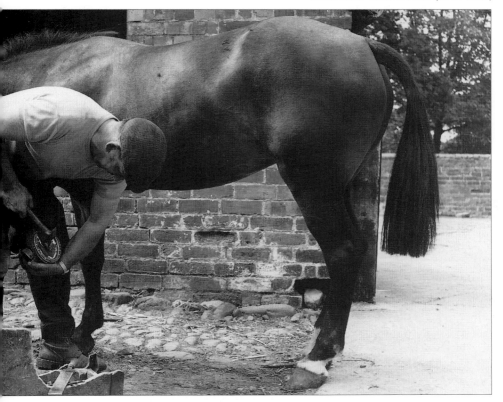

T. Edwards' smithy at Minsterley, now gone. He was also the wheelwright and undertaker, traditional services provided by local blacksmiths in many villages. In some places the old smithy became the new garage, as smiths diversified to survive in the modern world.
(Emily Griffiths – Snailbeach WI)

63

Shrewsbury & District Ancient Order of Foresters banner, paraded at Hadnall in 1951. This tradition, an annual Friendly Society event, had largely faded out by the 1930s and Hadnall Court, named Court General Hill after a local man, recreated the walk for their centenary. Unfortunately, the weather was very bad and the banner was torn by the wind.
(Ivy Bebb – Hadnall WI)

The Christmas party at Ford school in 1957. These were children of the New Elizabethan Age, with opportunities open to them that would have been unthinkable to children in 1900. The eager anticipation at the arrival of Father Christmas had not changed!
(Ford WI)

Jack Davies' cycle stand at the West Midlands Show in the 1950s. The 'West Mid' was a more local affair in those days. Jack Davies' shop is still selling bicycles in Chester Street, Shrewsbury.
(Muriel Painter – Shawbury WI)

65

Shrewsbury WI Market in their very early days in the old Market Hall in Shrewsbury. It provided a welcome opportunity for women to sell their produce, plants and cooked and baked goods to appreciative customers. The Market celebrated 40 years in business at Christmas 1997. (Lillian Hughes)

Above Morris dancers perform at Ludlow during the 1953 Coronation celebrations. All over the county towns and villages joined in games, teas, parties, dances and firework celebrations to welcome the young Queen.
(Mary Croxton – Lilleshall WI)

The Clive Hillside Players performing 'The Happiest Days of Your Life' in the village hall. The group was formed in 1949 by Jimmy Firth, a schoolmaster from Shrewsbury, and ran for about ten years. Amateur dramatics were very popular in many villages.
(Helen Phillips – Clive & Grinshill WI)

67

THE SIXTIES AND SEVENTIES

(1960 – 1979)

The Big Freeze that hit the country in January 1963 will long be remembered, equalling the winter of 1947 in ferocity. Coal supplies could not get through, firemen's hoses froze as they were used, and road salt was running out. Many isolated farms and villages were cut off for long periods. In February the thaw brought major flood warnings.

That spring also saw the effects of the Beeching Axe begin to bite into the county's railway system. More than 50 stations were cut and Shropshire was left with less than 100 miles of working track. Soon even the village bus had retired, heavily subsidised, to the main routes, sustained by schoolchildren and the elderly. Children were bussed to the new comprehensive schools which fortunately never got too big and by 1980 only the grammar schools at Shrewsbury and Newport survived, while village primary schools were already beginning to close as numbers decreased.

Farmers were being encouraged to produce more and more and farms grew larger. The industry survived the disaster of Foot and Mouth in 1967 when animals to the value of over £10 million were destroyed, most around Ellesmere, Prees and Wem. By 1980, with membership of the Common Market, food mountains were beginning to appear.

In 1963 the new power station was built at Ironbridge, its 670 foot chimneys making it one of the tallest structures in the United Kingdom. Other buildings reached for the sky too, multi storey car parks making their first appearance. New buildings were the fashion. There was a new Market Hall for Shrewsbury in 1965 and a year later a new Shirehall costing £1,800,000. Unfortunately not all new architecture was to prove popular in years to come.

Perhaps the biggest thing to hit Shropshire was the new town that became known as Telford. Starting with the simple idea of removing the industrial dereliction of Dawley, it became a radical concept stretching from Newport to the river Severn. It reclaimed for new development hundreds of acres of land, including the capping of over 3,000 mineshafts left from the coal mining and iron industries of the 18th and 19th centuries.

Some new building was welcomed. In 1965 Onibury in south Shropshire got a pub for the first time. A house called The Hollies was converted to a pub despite protests, principally from Lady Magnus Allcroft of Stokesay Court. Thirty years later Stokesay Court would be in the news when its owners died and an amazing treasure trove of collections was discovered.

The political map of Shropshire changed, accelerated by Telford, firstly in

Knockin's answer to Jodrell Bank.
(Dawn Herks – Knockin WI)

1960 – 1979

Jack Bedell and family at Bishops Castle in 1973. *The town was celebrating the granting of a charter by Elizabeth I in 1573. Dressing up proved as popular in this generation as when pageants enjoyed such a vogue earlier in the century.*
(Janet Preshous – Lydham, More & Snead WI)

1966 and then in 1972, when the market towns and the old boroughs such as Wenlock lost their independence. The new system had six district councils and a county council. The dominance of the landed gentry and the clergy, disguised as 'Independents' went for ever, and party politics ruled.

The mini skirt arrived, and parents found it impossible to appreciate their children's taste in music. Decimal currency was introduced in 1971 and immediately seemed to fuel inflation. Sex education was being experimented with in Shropshire schools 'by a married woman with children of her own'. Yet despite all the changes it was an adventurous time when anything seemed possible.

What must have been one of Shrewsbury's first supermarkets, in Whitchurch Road in the 1960s. This new 'American' style of shopping was welcomed for the choice it provided, though it would prove hard for the traditional corner shop to match.
(Alan Roberts – via Belvidere WI)

THEN & NOW
Battlefield Garage in 1930 and in the 1970s. The business was started in the early 1920s by E.B.H. Davenport.. He served his apprenticeship with Sentinel works, later Rolls-Royce and Perkins – once one of the town's largest employers, much of the site has now been sold off. The Battlefield Garage had a happier history and still trades to this day.
(Rachel Walton – Bicton & Oxon WI)

THEN & NOW

The blacksmith's shop at Stanton Lacy in 1920. The blacksmith Mr George Jones worked two days at Stanton Lacy and the rest of the week at Bromfield. In the early 1960s the interior of the shop was probably much the same as it had ever been. George Randle is working at the bench. Outside can be seen the BP petrol pump, a sign that this, like many other old forges, had survived the change from one form of transport to another.
(Barbara Tomkins – Bromfield WI)

Above Looking down over Smithfield Road, Shrewsbury. It is already a modern scene, with the high rise block in the distance.
(Alan Roberts – via Belvidere WI)

THE SIXTIES AND SEVENTIES (1960-1979)

The poplars at Bromfield were thriving in the early 1960s (right). They had been planted in the early 1900s by William Teague and his eldest son and were felled in 1968 in preparation for the building of the new bridge, shown here in the process of being erected.
(Barbara Tomkins – Bromfield WI)

Avenue Lodge, Linley in 1965. In the 1950s local authorities had offered grants to improve rural workers' cottages. The 18th-century cottage was reroofed, and an extension added using matching local limestone rubble.
(Margot Daniel – Lydham, More & Snead WI)

Floods at Frankwell in the 1960s. This was a notorious area for flooding and the inhabitants have suffered many times when the river has broken its banks. The bus forcing its way through was a Valley Motors bus from Bishops Castle, driven by Mr Len Higgs.
(Janet Preshous – Lydham, More & Snead WI)

THEN & NOW

In the early years of the century Mrs Hannah Perkin, of Perkins Beach, was midwife in this area of the Stiperstones. She also laid out the dead. In 1960 Beryl Hollingworth was a midwife covering the whole of south-west Shropshire on her own. She was allowed half a day off a week – provided there were no imminent arrivals. (Emily Griffiths – Snailbeach WI; Beryl Hollingworth – Westbury WI)

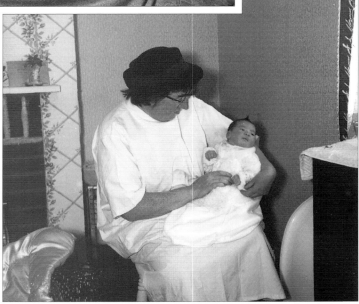

Condover village fete in 1962. Looking for a bargain never goes out of fashion!
(Shirley Addis – Condover WI)

The Bishops Castle steam rally in 1967. The show is still going strong but has moved from Bishops Castle to Onslow Park, near Shrewsbury, where it has taken on the official title of County of Salop Steam Rally.
(Rachel Walton – Bicton & Oxon WI)

Top left Timothy Walton delights in fishing for tiddlers in the river Severn at the Roughs, near the Mount, Shrewsbury. His mother did the same in her youth, armed with net, jam jar and old saucepan! (Rachel Walton – Bicton & Oxon WI)

Left *A Victorian picnic on 12th June 1977 to celebrate Queen Elizabeth's Silver Jubilee, at Ironbridge Gorge Blists Hill Museum.*
(Lily Speller – Coalbrookdale WI)

Above *Wem NFU cricket competition in the early 1960s. Nearly three quarters of all farmers belong to the NFU, which provides a vital link for farmers to meet for business and social events. Cricket, along with other recreations, was a part of the social scene.*
(Helen Phillips – Clive & Grinshill WI)

MODERN TIMES

(After 1980)

One of the greatest changes over the century has been the move from country to town. In 1986 the rural population of Shropshire totalled only one third of the county's population. There have been major losses in shops, churches, garages and primary schools in rural areas, to the detriment of country life.

When Telford was designated in 1968 to provide homes and jobs for people from the West Midlands, the population in the existing towns of Wellington, Oakengates, Dawley and Madeley was 75,000. Today it has grown to over 130,000 with capacity for more within the planned areas.

Farming has faced its greatest crisis since the foot and mouth outbreak, as BSE led to a sharp decline in beef sales. Farmers have also seen their markets moved out of town centres, severing the age-old connection between town and country.

In 1984 the well known rose grower and naturalist Hilda Murrell was murdered. The crime remains unsolved, though police believe she was the victim of a burglar at her Shrewsbury home. Conspiracy theories abound however, involving MI5 and her Royal Naval Commander nephew, or her anti-nuclear views, and led to books, TV and radio programmes and even a stage play.

Our way of shopping has changed, with out of town hypermarkets and ever-extending opening hours. Twenty-four hour shopping arrived over the Christmas period in 1997.

In April 1991 the county was shaken by an earthquake which caused some damage. Minor tremors have been felt from time to time through the century and quite a strong quake was recorded in 1916.

In 1998 Shrewsbury's Empire cinema closed after 75 years as plans for a new multi-screen cinema were made. Films have kept their popularity, despite the competition from television.

Shropshire's golden boy of football – Billy Wright – died in 1994. He was born in Ironbridge in 1924 and captained England in 1948.

Hunting has continued to find support as a country pursuit despite vociferous protest both locally and in Parliament. Ludlow Hunt was featured in a television documentary in 1998.

Computers have revolutionised every aspect of our lives. Children in 1900 used chalk and a slate at school, now they can draw on information from around the world at their fingertips. Much of life today would be regarded as miraculous were our ancestors to see it. How sad, therefore, that children today also face greater restrictions on their freedom than ever before.

Flowers laid in memory of Princess Diana at Pride Hill, Shrewsbury in 1997.
(Doris Broadhurst – Snailbeach WI)

After 1980

There are signs of a revival of the railway system. The Shrewsbury to London direct line link was reinstated in 1998. However, it will take more than this to curb the continued spread of the motor car – traffic growth is expected to be between 85% and 142% by the year 2025.

Gales over Christmas 1997 caused power cuts affecting 40,000 houses over three days. There were 21 Christmas Day babies born, many more than the daily average. The wind must have blown them all in, said the principal midwife at Shrewsbury.

One of today's most popular pastimes is gardening, and Percy Thrower MBE was at the forefront of promoting it as a hobby. He came to Shrewsbury in 1946 and fell in love with the area, and was famed for his award winning fuchsias at the Shrewsbury Flower Show. He died in 1988.

(Margaret Thrower)

81

THEN & NOW Lydham village before the First World War, with the driver of the horse and cart leaning on the bridge over the duck pond, and the same view today. Rose Cottage is on the left but only its name is the same. Lydham is still very much a village despite some new building.
(Margot Daniel, Janet Preshous – Lydham, More & Snead WI; Doris Broadhurst, Snailbeach WI)

THEN & NOW

High Street, Shrewsbury in the 1930s and as it is today. In 1997 a controversial traffic calming scheme narrowed the road, widened the pavements and installed cobbles in a bid to make the through-town route less attractive to vehicles.
(Doris Broadhurst, Snailbeach WI; Thelma Costley – Pulverbatch WI)

MODERN TIMES (AFTER 1980)

THEN & NOW
Butcher Row, Shrewsbury in the early years of the century and as it is today, hardly changed in its outlook. Great efforts have been made both here and in other old towns to keep such beautiful old buildings for residents of the next century to admire. (Age Concern, Shropshire; Margaret Francis – West Felton WI)

THEN & NOW

Shifnal in the early 1900s and the same scene today. The White Hart is almost unchanged, except for the loss of 'Good Stabling' above the yard door, but looks a little lonely without the cottages that butted up to it.

(Margaret Beddoes – Brockton WI)

A terrace of town cottages in Welsh Street, Bishops Castle, built in the 1980s. They were designed to blend with the railway workers' cottages on the left. For hundreds of years drovers brought cattle and sheep by this route from west and mid-Wales.
(Margot Daniel – Lydham, More & Snead WI)

At Perkins Beach, a miner's cottage showing the round stone chimney – the only one left in the area. People could claim squatter's rights if they could erect a hearth and chimney and have smoke rising from it by morning, and a round chimney was the simplest form.
(Emily Griffiths – Snailbeach WI)

The old school, Albrighton, being used as a polling station on 14th June 1984 for EEC elections.
(Mary Welsby – Albric WI)

The last day of Ludlow cattle market, 23rd January 1995. The move out of town was not entirely popular. Farmers' wives used to enjoy coming in to do their shopping but the market is now too far out to walk into the town centre.

The changing shapes of agriculture – grass patterns on fields, looking down from Grinshill heights 1994.
(Cynthia Martin – Clive & Grinshill WI)

Silaging at Hope, near Minsterley, in 1985 – a local farmer's first year with the new round bales. Today they are to be seen everywhere and the days of the thatched rick are long gone.
(Sue Johnson – Snailbeach WI)

The first West Midlands Agricultural Show was held in the Quarry, Shrewsbury in 1875. The 'West Mid' settled in the present showground at Berwick Road some 20 years later, where it has gone from strength to strength.
(Helen Phillips – Clive & Grinshill WI)

The delivery of an old fire engine to Blists Hill Museum, Ironbridge 1990. 'Living museums' have become a very successful part of the heritage leisure industry, giving people something of the atmosphere of times past.
(Mary Welsby – Albric WI)

The Arbor Tree at Aston on Clun in 1987, decorated with the flags of nations following an old village tradition. It was originated by the squire's son and each year is re-enacted by local schoolchildren. In 1995 the old tree was blown down and a new one planted.
(Sue Johnson – Snailbeach WI)

The Shrewsbury Quest Museum was set up in the shadow of the Abbey at Shrewsbury with an emphasis on the fictitious hero of the books of Ellis Peters, Brother Cadfael. Ellis Peters was the pen name of Edith Pargeter, who was born in Shropshire in 1913, and lived in the county all her life. She died in 1995.
(via Shrewsbury Quest)

Morris dancers (the Shropshire Bedlams and Martha Roden's Tuppenny Dish) at the Three Tuns, Bishops Castle, during the annual Midsummer Weekend in the late 1980s. Other activities include a rushbearing procession and a church service.
(Janet Preshous – Lydham, More & Snead WI)

Shooters at Broadlands in the early 1980s. The group was at the Broadlands Farm, Baschurch, home of Mr & Mrs J.R. Slater. Traditional country pursuits have continued in popularity.
(Helen Phillips – Clive & Grinshill WI)

Bishops Castle, Hope Valley and the surrounding areas play host to the annual Hope Valley Classic, one of the toughest cycle races in the country. It covers over 90 miles and competitors face some gruelling hills on the way. The white area to the side of the road is the remains of leadmining spoil heaps.
(Sue Johnson – Snailbeach WI)

THEN & NOW

On the see-saw in the Quarry, Shrewsbury in the late 1930s. Note the padlocks – this photo was taken on a Sunday. Today there is still a very popular children's playground here. The rules about playing on Sunday have disappeared but have been replaced by health and safety ones – there is now a rubberised playing surface.
(Thelma Costley – Pulverbatch WI; Doris Broadhurst – Snailbeach WI)

Above The VE Day Anniversary in May 1995, when veterans paraded to a church service in Bishops Castle. There were celebrations and services all over the county to mark this important date. (Janet Preshous – Lydham, More & Snead WI)

Below In 1986 workmen in a quarry in Condover found the skeleton of an adult woolly mammoth and two babies – 11,000 years old. Locals joined in the dig and there was an exhibition at RAF Cosford. (Barbara Harris – Condover WI)

Youngsters at a pancake race at Knockin in 1995. What a different world they face from that their great grandparents inhabited 100 years ago.
(Olwen Owen – Knockin WI)

The statue of engineer Thomas Telford that stands near the Law Courts in Telford town centre, and the site that is now filled by Telford New Town. It has brought not only homes, but shopping, commerce and entertainment, as well as employment opportunities in services and growth industries from abroad.
(Mary Croxton – Lilleshall WI; Ironbridge Museum)

Michael Clower

RIDING
FOR A FALL

CF

Cover design and layout by Jakobie de Wet (jakdesignco@gmail.com)
Book production by Christel Foord (cfoord@yebo.co.za)
Cover photo: www.shutterstock.com (rendered by Jak De_Sign)

Available as an ebook

More titles by Michael Clower
MICK KINANE – BIG RACE KING
CHAMPION CHARLIE
THE LEGEND OF ISTABRAQ
KINGS OF THE TURF

WITH SPECIAL THANKS TO

Nick Craven of Weatherbys
Nick Godfrey of Horse Racing Planet
(horseracingplanet.com)
James Burn of the Racing Post
and
my wife Tessa without whose encouragement this
book would never have seen the light of day

1

'One.....two......three.....hup.' The half-ton plus of power beneath my knees surged upwards and forwards over the thick black birch in perfect synchrony with my command. As his neck and front legs stretched, I let out several inches of rein to avoid interfering with his mouth. He hardly pecked on landing and, ears pricked, he galloped on towards the final fence as I gathered my reins once more.

I didn't need to look behind - I knew that I was several lengths clear - and I could sense that the pursuers were all of 20 metres behind. There was still the final energy-sapping Sandown hill to come but Brown River had plenty of stamina and was showing no sign of tiring. All he had to do was get over the fence and victory would be mine.

Suddenly, sixty metres from it, I heard a loud shout behind me. Some way behind but I could hear a horse coming. So could Brown River, and he dug deeper, seemingly into a more battling gear. The pursuer was closing - out of the corner of my eye I could now see him coming. Brown River's ears went back as the challenger got to his quarters. The grey horse was almost level now and then, without warning, he swerved violently left towards me, his jockey shouting at him as he tried to pull away from my horse. But the efforts of the man I recognised as Harry Jones were having no effect. Quite the opposite. The grey, showing the whites of his eyes, gave Brown River a hefty bump.

The fence was only two strides away. Knocked off balance at over 30mph, my horse struggled to take off and clear the fence. He skewed in mid-air and just about made it. I involuntarily threw out my right arm as I also battled to regain my balance. But, as Brown River landed, he stumbled. I could sense his knees buckling. I was pitched forward onto his neck, making things even more difficult for him. As he battled to get to his feet, mine came out of the stirrups and I was ejected out of the saddle and onto the grass.

Brown River regained the chase, his empty stirrups flapping like a whirling dervish. I looked up, cursing, as the grey horse headed towards the winning post. "Aah," a staggering pain ran through my left forearm as an aluminium-tipped hoof clipped me on its way past. I lay still, clutching my arm to ease the pain, fearing there were more horses still to come.

'You alright?' An ambulanceman came running towards me as I struggled to my feet, cursing my luck. 'Yea, nothing much anyway. Just my pride, I guess.'

As we walked towards the ambulance on the far side of the rails a rough-looking onlooker shouted: 'Fooking amacher. You'se couldn't ride a donkey on the beach,' and he spat into the ground as if to emphasise his point.

'Come on,' The ambulanceman grabbed hold of my good arm, steered me under the white railing and into the back of the ambulance. At the medical centre the doctor was waiting for me. 'What's the damage?' beamed a bespectacled bald man, seemingly delighted to be given a customer. He took hold of the arm I was clutching, rubbed his hand backwards and forwards over the damaged area as I tried not to wince. The last thing I wanted was to be stood down.

'Hmm. Don't like the look of that,' he said as I grimaced in pain. 'Could be something broken. Where do you live?'

I told him. 'Good, call into the hospital this evening and get it x-rayed. Might be hairline. When are you riding again?'

'Dunno, could be next Saturday. Not sure yet.'

'Hmm. I'm putting a note on your record that you must clear the doctor before your next ride.'

He looked up, hearing a knock on the door. A small man, with receding black hair brushed straight back, walked in. 'Mister Hutchinson.' The emphasis was all on the first word. "Stewards want you. Pronto.'

I hastily thanked the doctor and followed Lawrence Matthews through the weighing room. The ex-jockey seemed to have it in for me, but I knew I was by no means alone. 'He's a well-balanced individual – got a chip on both shoulders,' quipped a wag in the press room one day

'Wait here,' ordered Matthews as we reached the door with its 'Stewards Only' notice. Harry Jones was already there but, before I could ask him what the hell he had been doing, the door opened and a burly man in a navy windcheater came out, grinning broadly, gave a thumbs-up to Jones and strode off.

Lawrence Matthews beckoned me and Harry to follow him into a large room dominated by a long dark wooden table, a huge TV screen on the opposite wall and pictures of famous horses winning big Sandown races of yesteryear. 'Now gentleman, I want you to have a look at this film.' The tweed-suited, rather overweight speaker was clearly the most important of the four men seated along the table. The screen lit up and started with Brown River landing over the second last. It continued to the final fence but froze on an image of my mount crashing to the ground, my outstretched right arm nowhere near enough to save me.

But it showed very little of the winner, Grey Somali, crashing into Brown River. The picture switched to a sideways shot, again not revealing much as the camera was on the wrong side. The third film, though, showed the incident from the inside of the course – and showed it quite clearly with Harry Jones standing up in the irons as he tried in vain to keep his mount away from Brown River.

'Now Mr Hutchinson, just tell us what happened from your point of view.' The manner of the chairman of the stewards was friendly. I had never spoken to Christopher Mayhew before but I knew he was a successful businessman who owned a few racehorses and had ridden as an amateur in his youth. That was before his prominent blood vessels began indicating years of exposure to the weather or, as most people believed, an over- fondness for whisky.

I related how I was travelling so well that I thought I was sure to win if my horse jumped the last OK but Jones's mount came at me, knocked Brown River off-balance and caused him to fall.

The chairman of the stewards turned to Harry. 'Your version please, Mr Jones. '

'I was going much the better, sir.' He was an old hand at this. Being ultra-polite, even obsequious, was well known to get the stewards on your side. I cursed myself for having forgotten one of the basic tenets of racing inquiries, as the sing-song tones of Jones's Welsh origins continued its biased account. 'As the film clearly shows, sir, I was going much the better coming to the final fence," he repeated, as if for emphasis. 'When Grey Somali started to hang in, I pulled him away from the other 'orse. So there wasn't really much interference. Just a racing incident, I'd say sir."

'Hmm.' Christopher Mayhew looked down the table to his left and then at the man on his right. 'Thank you Mr Jones but Brown River did fall and he was interfered with as he was about to jump.'

It was as if Harry Jones had been waiting for this. 'Well, I didn't like to say anything sir…. but as you mention it, Mr 'utchinson 'ere is an amateur and not as fit as a pro. If one of us had been riding Brown River we would've balanced the horse properly and we wouldn't have fallen off.'

It was his trump card and he delivered it like a poker player with a full house. Seemingly, it was more than enough to convince Christopher Mayhew. 'Gentlemen,' he again looked at the men on each side of him. 'I think that concludes our inquiry.' He nodded at Lawrence Matthews. 'Result unchanged.'

Jones gave a slight bow and headed for the door. I moved to follow him out when Matthews stepped into my path and looked at the chairman.

"Ah yes. Nearly forgot. Mr Hutchinson, we want you to look at this bit of the film again.' It was the first shot and the out-of-sight camera operator froze it as my right arm was pointing to the heavens.

'Mr Hutchinson,' Mayhew began. 'We appreciate that, like a lot of us, you have a living to earn away from race-riding and so you perhaps are not as fit as a professional. You have ridden, what, three winners?'

'Plus ten in point-to-points, sir.' I remembered the politeness this time. Things were getting serious.

'Yes, of course. But on the racecourse I'm talking about – and we (he looked across at Matthews) feel that you must restrict yourself to amateur races until you have had more experience.'

I was stunned. This was a bitter blow. I was about to protest when, looking at the speaker's unsmiling face, it hit me that this was not the time or the place to argue, particularly with Matthews in the room. 'Sir.' I nodded at the chairman and walked out.

I glanced at my watch. Shit. Twenty minutes had passed since the end of the race. I'd be in more trouble now, and my arm was beginning to hurt like hell.

I went into the jockeys' room to put on my overcoat, hurriedly retrieved my phone from the security desk in the weighing room and glanced at the messages. As I feared, two were from Brett Marsh. 'Please ring. Urgent,' said the first. The second was the same except urgent had changed to very urgent.

Once outside – I didn't want the rest of the weighing room to hear what I was saying - I rang him. 'You OK?' But it wasn't my health that concerned him. 'We need news. The Major cried off sick.'

My mind hastily thinking through possibilities, I said: 'I'll see what I can get, and I'll ring you back. What about the race? Do I do the usual?

The tone of voice of the editor of *sports-all.com* changed from anxious to relaxed. 'Sure, do what it's worth. Should make a good story – even if it did cost me. Had a tenner on at 10-1. Thought I was going to collect too - or at least I did until the final fence.' I could hear the chuckle as he rang off.

The few in the press room greeted my arrival with predictable quips at my expense – mostly about glue and buying a bit of a land – as I got a list of big race entries out of my laptop case, carefully avoiding putting any pressure on my left forearm.

I compared the trainers' names on my list with those on the racecard – I needed people who were here at the racecourse, not those at home who I would have to ring. Fortunately there were half a dozen and, as my race was only the second on the card, most of them would be still on the racecourse.

I quickly wrote down the questions I wanted to ask and, after watching the next, I headed towards the winner's enclosure where a trainer in a helpful mood was virtually guaranteed. The florid features of Richard Robson were even more flushed than usual, his battered trilby pushed back as he told a group of admiring owners: "He will be worth an awful lot more by the time I've finished with him."

I waited until they were all on the point of heading to the members' bar. 'Richard. Well done. That was a good win.' Important to oil the wheels. Racing journalism, as I had quickly learned, is far from being all about writing. He beamed in my direction, probably searching for a name he couldn't remember.

'How is Mandable for the big one next Saturday?'

'Couldn't be better. You should have seen the way he went when I put him over four fences at home this morning.'

'Great. Did Robbie Bolton ride him?'

'Did indeed. Came up specially – and you know what he said?' Robson didn't wait for an answer. 'He said: "Bugger me, he's never been so well in his life. He won't just win next Saturday, he'll slaughter them."'

I thanked the trainer as he headed off to his liquid refreshment, his grateful owners hot on his heels, while I hastily wrote down his confident words in my notebook. I could already envisage his colourful turn of phrase livening up my copy.

John Barnard, intercepted while taking his jockey's saddle to the boxes on the far side of the parade ring to prepare for the next, was more conventional and more reserved about Gallant George's preparation for the same race, the Hilton Chase, here next weekend. 'He only ran three weeks ago, as you know, so we haven't had to do an awful lot with him. But what he's done, he's done well.'

'Give him a decent chance?'

'Yes, obviously. He's one of the favourites, the trip will suit him but I just hope we don't get too much more rain.'

Back in the press room, I wrote his comments down and then went through them, and those of Richard Robson, to make sure I could read them. My handwriting was getting worse by the week and, the more in a hurry I was, the more illegible the writing.

I only half watched the next. My mind was on what I was going to ask Oliver Chester-Beatty. He was classified under difficult, and not just by me. The Newmarket trainer, better known for his classic-winning exploits on the Flat, had a fancied contender in the Hilton. He also had a runner in the next.

I fell into step with him as he left the weighing room and headed purposefully for the saddling boxes. 'Hi Oliver.' My manner was, I hoped, professionally friendly. He didn't respond. 'How is Big Thomas for next Saturday?'

After a lengthy pause, the small, rather ferret-faced man suddenly stopped and looked me straight in the eye without saying a word. I could see this was going to be tricky. His gaze travelled down to what could be seen of the boots and breeches beneath my overcoat. 'You were robbed.'

This time it was me who didn't answer. 'That grey horse was dancing around all over the place in the winner's enclosure, his eyes were popping out of his head - and he was pouring sweat.'

I wasn't sure how to answer, and I needed to get him back on track. 'I didn't see that. I had to go straight to the medical room. About Big Thomas. Is he in good shape?'

Much to my surprise Chester-Beatty went into a lengthy discourse about how the horse had been laid out for next Saturday's race since the start of the season, how he had come on considerably since his prep run and that he was strongly fancied.

As the trainer spoke, I repeated his words in my mind in a bid to memorise them. I knew that, if I began to write them down, he would clam up - while producing a tape recorder would stop the flow before it even started. As he came to the end of the Big Thomas update, I decided to throw caution to the wind.

'And how is Lazarus Luke progressing?' Chester-Beatty reverted to his earlier stony silence and looked me unsmilingly full in the face. Just when I was thinking I should have been grateful for what I'd got and called it a day, he smiled. 'That was one question I hoped you wouldn't ask.'

This time it was my turn to say nothing – except for an enquiring glance. The trainer took a noticeably deep breath. Clearly something had happened to next season's 2,000 Guineas favourite.

'He knocked his off-hind last week and there was some swelling that wouldn't go down. We had him scanned and, while it's not serious, he is going to have to be on the easy list for eight weeks.'

'So he should still be able to make the Guineas?'

'I think so – at least I hope so. But it's not what you want with a horse as good as that.'

Chester-Beatty turned and resumed his path to the stables. I again fell in beside him. 'Oliver, you were saying about Grey Somali. Do you think he had been given something?'

The trainer stopped in his tracks a second time. This time he grinned. 'That's something for you to find out, isn't it?

You're the journalist, not me.'

Thirty minutes later, back in the press room, the first of my articles already filed, my mobile buzzed as I was drinking a cup of tea and eating what I regarded as a well-earned sandwich, the first sustenance I'd had since breakfast. 'Great stuff,' said the unsigned message. I grinned. I knew Brett Marsh would like the copy.

Now I could afford to take my time with the race report. I read through the stewards' inquiry on the British Horseracing Authority website and, rather more anxiously, searched for the supplementary for the restriction on my future riding. There wasn't one. But I knew it was only a matter of time. My mind filled with an alarming picture of all the races I would miss, and the dreams and ambitions that were going to be shattered.

I forced myself to concentrate on the present, and the stab of pain from my arm actually helped. I looked up the race result and I was astonished. Grey Somali, who I'd regarded as a no-hoper before the race, had been backed from 20-1 to 4-1 second favourite. Clearly somebody knew he was going to leave his previous form behind, and seemingly there was a powerful financial reason behind the trainer's thumbs-up as he came out of the stewards' room. I went back to the report. The trainer, Bob Arrows, had explained that he had changed Grey Somali's food since his last run, the horse had improved markedly in condition and had been expected to run well. The stewards had noted his explanation rather than accepting it. In other words, they didn't believe him but there was nothing they could do about it other than place it on record to use against him should he try the same explanation with another horse.

Some ninety minutes later, plus a further cup of tea and another sandwich, I logged on to the website. 'Our man robbed of victory by final fence fracas' screamed the large headline above my story. I was less happy about the photograph – Brown River on his knees and me with my right arm raised to the heavens as I was about to be fired out of the saddle. If Lawrence Matthews needed any further ammunition, he had it now.

I skimmed through the copy. Thank God. Brett didn't seem to have changed anything. I'd been careful to say nothing about the shout, or what Chester Beatty had implied - I'd been in trouble with *sports-all.com*'s libel lawyers before – but, as a journalist, you could never be sure that your editor hadn't decided to spice it up a bit.

The picture - and what Christopher Mayhew had said - worried me. Amateur races-only meant not many more opportunities for me until the hunter-race season began in earnest in February, and then the horses had to be qualified by going hunting. My two were racehorses, not hunters – and I knew full well that one of the main reasons *sports-all. com* had given me a contract was because I was in a position to report on the racing like few other journalists.

Furthermore, and to me this was even more important, my over-riding ambition was to follow in the footsteps of some of the most famous race-riding scribes like Marcus Armytage, who had won the Grand National, and Lord Oaksey who had gone close in the greatest steeplechase of all. How would I ever get the chance if I was officially regarded as not good enough to ride against the professionals?

I was rapidly descending into a state of near-despair, and it somehow seemed to start my arm off again. The pain was intense. I needed to get to hospital. There were still two races left but I decided I would have to chance it. If something dramatic happened, I wouldn't be here. I packed up my case, nodded at the two journalists at the far end of the room gossiping about God knows what, and headed for the car park.

2

The sirens and flashing lights hit me as I neared the Royal Berkshire's multi-storey. Two ambulances, clearly in a hell of a hurry, screeched to a halt outside Accident & Emergency. The drivers, and their fellow-uniformed passengers, leapt from their respective doors and hurried round to open up the back. Nurses, and what I presumed to be hospital porters, appeared from inside the building as a third ambulance, also siren blaring and warning light flashing, hurtled on to the scene.

I got out of the car and hurried over. 'You can't park there, mate,' said one of the porters.

'What's happened?'

'Six-car pile-up on the M4 – and shift that fucking car.'

I moved it round the corner, out of the porter's sight, and hurried back to the building. One glance inside and I could tell I would be there for hours. There were several people already waiting in the casualty reception, while all attention was centred on the new arrivals. Suddenly my arm didn't seem so bad. I would go to the doctor in the morning.

My Kennet Walk flat was only ten minutes away. A stiff brandy later, I was watching the recording of my race. At the second last I was indeed at least five lengths clear and, while Grey Somali was not really under pressure, he wasn't exactly cruising. Indeed Harry Jones picked up his whip only a few strides later. But he was soon narrowing the gap. The TV showed no more of the bump than the first stewards' room shot although, freezing the picture, showed me looking less than elegant – and arm outstretched - as I was forcibly rolled off. There was no winner's enclosure shot – the action had switched to the all-weather at Wolverhampton by that stage.

Dispiritedly I made some supper and ate it considering the implications for my future. I looked again at the BHA website. Still no report on my riding. Maybe they would wait until the office staff were in on Monday before finalising that. But, no matter when it came, my dreams and ambitions – if not my job too - were going to be shattered.

I aimlessly flicked through the TV channels, trying to find something to take my mind off my problems and the pain returning in my arm. I went to the bathroom cupboard and studied the label. As I feared – 'not to be taken with alcohol.'

Rolling up my sleeve, I was horrified. What had not already turned black was as red as my scarlet jumper. Gingerly, I pressed various parts on the affected forearm. The intensity of the pain convinced me that something was broken. Should I have stayed at the hospital? Should I go back now? Supposing I got stopped by the police? What a stupid sod I was to have drunk that brandy.

An hour's soak in the bath helped the agony, even if not my mood. I went to bed fearing a long sleepless night but, much to my surprise, the clock said nearly 3.00 am when I woke. The arm was hurting so badly that, throwing all printed warnings to the wind, I took two painkillers. I sat down at the kitchen table and went back over what Oliver Chester-Beatty had told me. That winner's enclosure behaviour – and the trainer's words – could mean only one thing. Grey Somali had been doped to win.

His trainer would have known that the horse would be tested – all winners were as a matter of routine – and the testing process was widely considered to be foolproof.

Unless? Supposing the trainer had come up with something new that was not on the BHA's banned substance list? There were always rumours of such things and Grey Sombrero's winner's enclosure behaviour was a giveaway. But how was I going to prove it? And how was I going to write about it without the BHA's lawyers – not to mention Bob Arrows' – taking me to the cleaners and getting me sacked?

The painkillers must have done their job because, when I went back to bed, I fell asleep almost immediately. The alarm woke me at 7.00am and ninety minutes later I pulled up outside the surgery. Eliza Pendragon, the receptionist who ran the practice like a modern-day version of Attila The Hun – my sister referred to her as the dragon - had a soft spot for me and I knew she would fit me in no matter how booked up they might be.

But she wasn't at the reception desk. In her place was a good-looking blonde girl in her early twenties wearing a white roll-neck top and, so far as I could see, close-fitting black trousers. 'How can I help?' she smiled.

'Er..' I was verbally thrown off balance. 'Is Eliza in?'

"She's on holiday,' the smile seemed almost dazzling. 'You will have to make do with me. Do you have an appointment?'

'Er.. no. But I've come to see Dr Richardson.'

'He's in. What name shall I say?' I told her and she wrote it down. 'Do I tell him what it's about?'

'Yea. I got kicked yesterday.... and my arm is in a bad way.' I touched it as if to indicate the problem, and the expression of pain on my face seemed to trigger concern on that of the receptionist.

'You could be lucky. The 8.30 is with him now and the 9.00am has rung to say she will be 15 minutes late. So I might be able to slot you in.'

It was my turn to smile. 'That's great. Thank you very much.' I glanced round for a nearby seat, picked up a copy of *Hello* from the magazine table and pretended to read it. She was attractive, even more than I first thought. Periodically I glanced round the large waiting room, trying not let my increasing-fascination become too obvious.

I did my best to look as if I was studying the framed qualification certificates beside the door of each of the four doctors. Dr Richardson's door opened and I could hear his voice seconds before he ushered out an elderly lady with a walking stick, and took her by the arm towards the blonde. "Mrs Edwards needs another appointment in a fortnight, Emma. Will you fix her up at a time that suits her?'

He turned round the register on her desk, put on his glasses and studied it. 'Who's next? Ah Rod.' My brother-in-law looked up and beamed in my direction. 'Didn't expect to see you today. Thought you'd be off to Newbury or wherever.

Come in.'

I followed the tall, white-coated figure with wavy brown hair into the surgery, and took the seat he directed me to while he settled himself in his chair on the other side of the desk. Stuart Richardson had married my sister soon after he qualified and bought himself into the busy partnership about five years ago. 'So, what brings you here?'

I explained about my arm, what the racecourse doctor had said and the pain I had been experiencing. Surprise, surprise – that had now disappeared and I found myself wondering why I had come.

'Let's get it x-rayed.' Stuart stood up. 'Come with me." He led the way back into the reception area. Emma returned my smile, making me feel better still. Once inside the door marked 'Doctors Only' I was instructed to take my shirt off and lay my injured arm along the leather-covered rest of a fearsome-looking machine. It was not dissimilar to the one you put your face up against when your dentist needs to take an x-ray.

He gently pushed the arm into the position he wanted, told me not to move and pressed some out-of-sight button before repeating the process twice more, each with the arm at different angles.

'Right, let's return to the surgery.' Emma was standing up with her back to me, the black trousers tight around her shapely rear.

Stuart fiddled with his computer for a couple of minutes before a much-enlarged x-ray picture appeared on the large screen attached to the far wall. He stood up and studied it. 'This is the root of your particular evil.' He pointed to a white section of bone with a ruler from his desk. 'See this little fellow here? It's only a tiny crack but press it and you will go through the roof.'

'How long will it take to heal?'

My brother-in-law grinned. 'I thought you'd ask that. I suppose you've got another race coming up?'

I wasn't sure about that. February was three months away. But, I reminded myself, I needed to be positive. 'Could be in a fortnight.'

Stuart transferred his attention from the screen to his patient, and took off his glasses. 'Going to take a bit longer than that. Strictly speaking I should send you down to casualty to have it put in plaster.' He smiled as he saw the pained expression on my face. 'I think we can get away with a splint to keep any pressure off, and bandaging to hold it in place. You might be OK to resume in four weeks. But,' he looked me straight in the eye. 'No riding in the meantime and nothing that is going to put any pressure on the injury. OK?'

I nodded my agreement and looked on as, for the next ten minutes, he bathed and cleaned the bruises, smoothed on antiseptic cream, wrapped the affected area with three thin layers of gauze, covered the cracked section with a piece of white plastic, and the whole area with a bandage. Telling me to come back in a week, he took me to the delightful Emma and told her to fit me in at the same time next Saturday.

'Could we make it fairly early, Emma? I might have to go to Haydock that day.'

'Sure,' she turned over a few pages in the appointments book. "8.30am OK?

'Perfect Emma. Thank you.' Using her name made me feel good and, judging by the smile I got in return, it went down well with her too.

The Sandown press room was hardly recognisable from the previous day's almost deserted, atmosphere-missing four walls by the time I got there an hour before the first. It was packed to the gills with half the racing journalists in the country. It wasn't the big race that attracted them so much as the sponsor's lunch. For many of them a sumptuous meal, and unlimited free alcohol, was a far bigger draw than the actual racing.

'Bad luck yesterday Rod. I thought you had it in the bag at the second last.' Charles Cavendish, *sports-all.com*'s chief racing correspondent, beamed as he came up to me and shook hands. There was always a lot of hand-shaking on the racecourse – just as well it was my left arm that was kicked –and I noticed that today it was the turn of the Household Cavalry. 'The Major', as he was known, as well as the pseudonym under which his widely-read tipping pieces appeared, always wore a club or old school tie –usually the black with light blue stripes reserved for Old Etonians but today it was navy and maroon stripes.

Tall, grey-haired and distinguished-looking, Charles was something of a legend on the racecourse. The son of a Grand National-winning trainer, he rode the winner of the Grand Military Gold Cup when still a serving officer and these days was famed for his successful tipping pieces. He had won the naps table award in four of the past five years and his success was widely attributed to his being on such good terms with most of the top trainers - their views on the chances of their horses were widely quoted in his articles. For most of his long journalistic career he had written for the top national dailies but, when his main employer folded less than two years ago, *sports-all.com* gratefully snapped him up.

A man of considerable charm, he was revered by punters as well as by many of the racehorse owners, and no small number considered it a sign of social recognition to be seen talking to him. However I was one of the few people aware of the agonies he had been through in his personal life. A few years ago his only child, a daughter who had clearly inherited all the equine talent of her father and her grandfather and was widely tipped for the top in the world of three-day eventing, damaged her spine in a fall at Badminton. She was paralysed from the waist down. Last year Charles's wife, to whom he was clearly devoted, died after being ill for some time.

Despite these setbacks, he remained outwardly cheerful and he had gone out of his way to help me in my burgeoning journalistic career, introducing me to useful contacts, frequently offering me advice and pointing me in the right direction. I looked upon him as a friendly uncle and often consulted him when I had problems.

'Charles, I want a word. Let's go outside, away from all the prying ears.'

'Sure.' He followed me out and round the corner. I told him what Chester-Beatty had said about Grey Somali's appearance and behaviour in the winner's enclosure and about that loud shout after the second last.

'Are you sure it was Harry Jones who shouted?'

His question sowed the first seeds of doubt. I had assumed

it came from Grey Sombrero's jockey. But had it? The more I thought about it, the more I realised it could have been one of a number of the other riders. 'Well, I think it was him. His horse was the one who responded.'

'Jockeys do funny things, you know Rod. True, some shout but I've known others who whistled at their mounts when they wanted them to quicken, and quite a number make clicking noises with their tongues. Anything to attract their horse's attention and make him realise he is required to go faster.'

'But what about the way the horse was dancing about in the winner's enclosure - with his eyes popping out?'

'That's suspicious alright. But think about it. If the trainer has been giving the horse anything, it will show up in the dope test and he will be in big trouble.'

'Hmm,' I nodded. 'But I'm going to follow it up. Make a fascinating story, if nothing else.'

Charles laughed but, putting his hand on my right arm, he said, much more seriously: 'Rod, remember Brett's Ten Commandments.'

'You mean about the bookies?' It was my turn to laugh.

'Exactly. Thou shalt not upset the bookmakers, and the second Commandment is likewise, and all the others too.'

The bookmakers were *sports-all.com*'s main source of revenue. Each sport, and almost every page, carried advertisements showing the latest prices for coming events and championships. Racing, traditionally the bookmakers' main sphere of operation, had easily the most advertisements and that was why Brett employed two journalists rather than the single one for other sports.

'You think there is a bookmaker involvement with Grey Somali?'

'In my experience there is invariably a bookmaker involved in one way or another,' came the reply. 'If there is not a bookie actually involved then, whoever is doing it, is using his inside knowledge to back whatever is going to win.'

I'd become increasingly aware that we had an audience, and that it was growing. The slowness of my latest response encouraged a middle-aged man in a mac to step forward. 'Charles,' he began. 'What's your bet of the day?'

His question seemed to act as a signal for the others to crowd round the champion tipster like bees around a hive, several of them asking for tips of their own. Charles was in his element. Pausing only to look over their heads and call out to me 'see you up there,' he spoke earnestly to his fans who eagerly soaked up every word as if it was gospel.

They ignored me as I retreated back into the press room. The crowd there was thinning rapidly as the hacks made their way to the top of the grandstand where their drinks and food awaited.

I sat down and leafed through the racecard. The name I was looking for was not on the list of stewards but he did have a runner in the second. He would also be at the reception but I needed to speak to him when he was on his own.

Trevor Brownson, my own trainer, had only one runner – Bejaysus in the fifth. I needed to speak to him too. And there were the prospective interviewees. I made a note that Robbie Bolton, the rider of the favourite in next Saturday's Hilton Chase, had mounts in every race bar the third and the last. Alec Smith, the jockey on second favourite Gallant

George, would be free during the second and the fourth, the big one, where his mount had gone lame. I wrote down a string of questions in my notebook before going over to the reception. Fortunately it was a buffet so I was able to get what I wanted without having to wait for each course, and be finished before the first race.

Fifteen minutes before the second a trilby-hatted Christopher Mayhew, binoculars hanging from the leather strap across the chest of his camel-coloured overcoat, was in the parade ring with a smartly-dressed woman I assumed to be his wife. Both were talking to the trainer and jockey of their runner in the two-mile handicap hurdle. I positioned myself near the exit until the jockey was legged into the saddle and the group headed my way. I ducked under the rails and walked towards them. 'Hi, Christopher,' I said, smiling, as I tried to convey an impression likely to bring a favourable response.

'Rodney, good to see you,' came the reply as he shook me by the hand before introducing me to his wife as a 'top racing journalist and an up-and-coming amateur.'

So far so good. I walked with them towards the grandstand, explaining that I had studied the re-run and it made me look a bit amateurish. 'But I wouldn't want you to think that I was unfit or anything. My horse was knocked off balance by the winner cannoning into him as he was about to jump the fence.'

'Yes, that's how we saw it too. You had no chance of staying in the saddle. Bloody bad luck.'

'But Christopher,' I replied, trying not to sound anxious. 'Am I alright to continue riding in professional races?'

'Don't see why not?' He seemed surprised that I had asked the question.

'Well, it was just what you said at the end of the inquiry. And Lawrence Matthews.....' Mayhew, raising his hat to a woman in a striking red coat, stopped in his tracks and smilingly gave me his full attention. 'Forget it. Sometimes we volunteer stewards get a bit press-ganged by the professional officials. That's why they still have people like me. To see fair play.'

'That's great.' I didn't know if the relief was showing in my voice but I certainly felt it. 'You've made my day.' It was my turn to shake his hand.

'If I'd been restricted every time I called a cab I would never have ridden a winner. Liked your article, by the way. Gripping stuff.' He stepped onto the escalator, wife in close attendance and giving me a brief wave as they headed for the VIP boxes at the top of the stands.

I felt on top of the world, confident I could tackle anything no matter how difficult which was just as well because Robbie Bolton didn't want to talk. He took his time about coming to the door when the white-coated attendant (on duty to stop the likes of me entering the hallowed sanctum of the jockeys' room, at least on days when I was not riding) called out his name.

Far from repeating the 'won't just win, he'll slaughter them,' he looked from me to the tape recorder with a decided lack of enthusiasm. I explained how I was writing about the Hilton Chase and asked if he still felt as confident as he had been after putting the horse over four fences the previous day.

'Dunno really,' came the unenthusiastic reply. 'It's a big race and it's a handicap. Anything could win and, well, I'd rather not say anything if it's all the same with you.'

In ordinary circumstances I would have prompted him with a few general questions of the 'Got a good chance? You hopeful?' type but I was too buoyed up to settle for anything like that. 'Come on Robbie,' I urged. 'This is your race, you've won it four times in the last eight years and you've got an army of fans out there all crying out for a few confident words from their hero.'

'Yea, I suppose you're right.' And with that he spoke with increasing enthusiasm about Mandable, the form the horse was in and how well he had been going at home.

'And the opposition? Which ones are you most afraid of?'

'They'll need to be fucking good to beat me – and none of them jump as well as my bugger, I can tell you.' He glanced down at the tape recorder and grinned. 'That OK?'

Half an hour later Alec Smith needed no such second bidding to talk about Gallant George. A small wiry man of about twenty, he was a rising star and had already learned the value of publicity. He spoke into the tape recorder with all the enthusiasm of a politician at election time. Encouraged by this, I asked him questions about his background, early days in racing and his ambitions. I ended up with enough material for a full length feature, and he seemed delighted when I told him it would be on the website within the next few days.

The forecast rain was just starting as I hopped jauntily down the weighing room steps and thirty minutes later it was clear that it had set in for the day. The stable lad leading

Bejaysus round the parade ring was well protected by light waterproofs of the type used by golfers but there was no sign of Trevor Brownson. Indeed I hadn't expected him to be here. My trainer was a reluctant racegoer, reckoning his work was in the stables at home, not in the shop window of the racecourse. Willie Monaghan, his Irish travelling head lad, came into the ring with the jockeys and carrying a rolled up blanket. He seemed pleased to see me as he shook hands. 'Howya Rod? You OK after yesterday?'

He started chatting about Brown River, how well he had run and how unlucky he had been before I had a chance to ask if Trevor would be at home tomorrow. 'Jaysus. The boss at Worcester? You must be joking. We've only got the two runners so it'll be me on the road again by half eight.'

I hurried off through the increasing rain to the sanctity of the press room where most of the seats were taken up with various scribes tapping out their copy, some with a glass of whisky alongside their laptops and some, even though it was expressly forbidden by the notices on the long tables, with a cigarette between their lips. Only when somebody bumped my arm did I realise that I hadn't thought about the crack and the bruising for hours. Clearly Stuart had done a good job.

Nobody took the slightest notice of the last race on the card, being played out on the big screens at each end of the room, as I sorted through my notes and worked out that I only needed a couple more interviews and I would have enough for the website in the days leading up to the Hilton. Tomorrow could well complete the picture.

3

'Here's the guv'nor now.' Manch Wilkinson, the lad who looked after both my horses, nodded in the direction of the concrete path leading from the house to the stables and the stocky, rugged-looking figure in corduroys and thick khaki-coloured jersey with leather patches on the elbows. Trevor Brownson, almost bald, still dressed like the army officer he once was.

'Morning Rod,' he said before switching his attention to Manch. 'Did Brown River eat up?' Despite being assured that the horse had consumed every last nut, the trainer looked concerned. 'Had quite a hard race on Friday,' he explained to me. 'Even though you came off at the last.'

Trevor's dislike of putting up amateurs – even when they owned the horses – was never far below the surface, and I thought I detected a quickening of interest when I explained about my cracked arm ruling me out for the next three to four weeks. 'So I don't want either of mine running till I'm back.'

'Hmm.' He contemplated in silence for what seemed like half a minute. 'Brown River could benefit from a short break,' he said eventually. 'But I might give Ezekiel a blow-out in a fortnight or so. He's a stuffy sort and a race should put him spot on for when you're back.'

His attention was caught by a red Aston Martin coming fast up the drive towards the house, and he winced as the car pulled up sharply, spraying gravel in all directions. 'My bloody brother,' he muttered as he headed back to the house.

I knew something about Jimmy Brownson from a recent write-up I'd seen on one of the financial pages. A flamboyant company doctor – almost a contradiction in terms according to the writer of the article - he was much in demand when businesses were in danger of going under. He had a track record of turning them round and taking a stake in the company as part of his substantial remuneration. He was now investing in racing and bloodstock.

The journalist who interviewed him got more in a single session than I'd learned about his elder brother in the two-plus years that he had been training my horses. Trevor had refused my requests to be interviewed about his life – 'I hate that sort of thing' – and I knew his army career held more of interest than most of his brother officers. He had been awarded the Military Cross for some act of bravery in South Armagh, said to be risking his own life by defusing a particularly powerful IRA pipe bomb, so saving the lives of his platoon, even though he had had no specialised training. But, whenever I tried to bring it into the conversation, he would shrug his shoulders and say: 'Just one of those things you do when you don't have much choice. End of story.'

On leaving the army he had gone into racing and become a successful jumps trainer but now he was expanding into the Flat, thanks in no small part to his brother's expensive purchases.

Sunday morning was open house for the owners of his Lambourn stable with wife Sarah supervising the preparation of a buffet lunch. I gave Manch £20, thanked him for all he was doing for my horses and headed towards the house where the dark-haired Sarah, looking particularly good in cream jersey and tartan skirt, greeted me with a kiss and a hug. 'Sorry, maybe I shouldn't have done that. Trevor told me about your damaged arm.'

I liked Sarah. She always seemed genuinely pleased to see me and she took an interest in the races in which I was riding – unlike her husband who often left me with the impression that, were it not for the training fees I was paying, he would be better off without my horses.

"You know the form, Rod. First door on the left, help yourself to a drink and lunch will be on the table in about half an hour.'

There were a dozen or so other owners in what was normally the dining room. I didn't recognise any of them but, nodding at those I passed, I helped myself to a beer and glanced around at the oil paintings of the most famous of the horses Trevor had trained.

'Rod, I've got some people I want you to meet.' Sarah took my arm and steered me in the direction of a couple in their sixties, a bald man in a check suit and a smartly-dressed grey-haired lady. 'George, Gisela. Can I introduce you to

Rod Hutchinson? Rod is a very good amateur rider and a top racing journalist. You must have read his articles on the *sports-all.com* website.' Sarah always made me feel ten feet tall.

We shook hands as she continued: 'The Grahams have got a runner in the Hilton on Saturday. Not from here unfortunately ....but maybe next year.'

George Graham said he followed The Major's tips – 'He's won me a fair bit of money' - but it was Gisela who did most of the talking: her grandfather had owned horses, she said. He had the runner-up in the Derby in the 1940s and she had taken over his colours 'now that George has sold his business and we've got time to enjoy ourselves.'

Their Hilton runner was one of the outsiders but their enthusiasm was infectious. I told them not to move while I got my tape recorder from the car. Asking Sarah if I could borrow her sitting room for ten minutes, I ushered them out of the dining room and interviewed them away from all the noise. They seemed delighted to talk about their lives and how excited they were by having their first big race runner.

The buffet was spread out all over the long mahogany table by the time we returned and, as I helped myself to a couple of slices of beef, some roast potatoes and an equally appetising selection of veg, I became aware of a fair-haired man in his forties holding forth about the profits that could be made from racehorses running on the Flat. 'Of course, you've got to invest quite a bit and know what you're doing but it's quite possible to turn a hundred grand yearling into a multi-million pound stallion.'

Sarah, with a knowing glance and eyebrows raised in my direction, interrupted the flow. 'Jimmy. Have you met Rod

Hutchinson?' She repeated the flattering spiel with which she had introduced me to the Grahams. 'Jimmy is Trevor's younger brother and he has quite a few horses now – but he's a more of a Flat man.'

Jimmy Browne seemed more than happy to include me in his audience although I couldn't say the sentiment was mutual. I had met a number of know-alls like him who couldn't understand why the rest of racing was so stupid. After ten minutes I managed to break away with the excuse that I had articles to write and must be getting back. I thanked Sarah for the lunch, and was hugged and kissed in return. I looked round for Trevor. 'He's already gone,' she laughed. 'Nap time. Doesn't matter who's here. Nothing and nobody gets in the way of his afternoon sleep.'

As I drove away I thought back to what the trainer had said about Brown River having had a hard race. Manch – I didn't know his Christian name; everyone called him Manch because he came from Manchester - had told me that the horse was bouncing on Saturday morning. 'You wouldn't think he'd had a race, he was that full of himself. Ate every last cube on Friday night and again yesterday.'

So why was Trevor telling me the opposite?

It was shortly after 9.00am when I parked outside the Reading surgery. The arm was healing well – a lot of the bruising seemed to have gone when I'd taken off the plastic and gingerly peeled back the gauze on Sunday evening. But Monday was Stuart's day off and that was partly why I was there; I didn't want my visit to get back to my sister, particularly if Emma said no.

Several mothers, and what seemed like a whole host of their children, filled almost every available chair but my eyes were more on the reception desk – and I was taken aback to find the dragon in her usual seat. 'Hi Eliza,' I greeted her, trying to recover my composure. 'How was the holiday?'

'Fine. Stuart's not in today. Will you see one of the other doctors?'

'Er… no. I haven't come for that.'

The dragon raised an eyebrow and cursed as the phone at her elbow rang. 'Only been back an hour and the bloody thing's hardly stopped. New Street Surgery, Eliza speaking, how can I help?'

She told the caller which of the doctors were on duty, and the various times they would have a free twenty minutes, while I looked round the waiting room wondering how I was going to get what I wanted.

The dragon booked the caller for 11.00am. 'Sorry Rodney. Where were we? Who did you say you would like to see?'

'It's not that, Eliza. I was here on Saturday and Emma booked me back with Stuart this Saturday. But I'm not sure what time.'

'Didn't she give you a card? Typical. It's always a mess when I come back from holiday.' She leafed through the appointments book. 'Here we are. 8.30am.'

She reached for the pile of appointment cards on the top right-hand corner of the desk, filled in the top one and handed it over as the phone rang again. 'New Street Surgery, Eliza speaking, how can I help?'

The conversation showed every sign of being a long one -

from what I could make out somebody's child had come out in spots. Looking round I found a vacant chair, picked up a magazine from the table and sat down, considering how best to frame my question. But no sooner had the dragon put the phone down, it rang again. "New Street Surgery, Eliza speaking......'

I was just giving up and getting out of my chair when her hand waved me back. When she ended the conversation, appointment booked for 2.30pm, she put down the receiver and promptly picked it up again preventing further incoming calls. 'Sorry Rodney,' she called out. 'Was there something else?'

I got up and walked across to the desk, conscious that all the mothers were watching with interest. 'Er, there was actually Eliza. The girl that was here on Saturday, will she be back?'

'I doubt it.' She gave me a knowing smile. 'She would have come from an agency. That's what we do these days when I'm away.'

'What's the name of the agency?'

Another knowing smile. 'Sorry Rodney. I wasn't involved. But Stuart will know. He'll be here tomorrow. Give him a ring.'

I went back to the car, my mind in a daze. If I did ring Stuart he would be bound to tell my sister; he knew just how interesting she found my love life.

I ought to return to the flat and get on with playing the tapes. Every word of every interview had to be typed out. I was sure other journalists didn't go to such lengths but I'd found that, if you skipped the bits you thought wouldn't be of any use, you invariably discovered you were wrong and had to go back through the whole interview to find them. Much better, although more time-consuming, to type out the lot.

Many people, I knew, wrote the relevant bits out by hand but that wouldn't work with my writing – I would be forever struggling to read what I'd written when I needed to give my full attention to writing the story. I'd done the tapes for Robbie Bolton and Alec Smith when I got home on Sunday afternoon and first thing this morning I'd drafted the Bolton piece. It wasn't due in until Tuesday morning. I could afford to take a few hours off.

The address in the *Horses In Training* book was Wantage but Google indicated that Bob Arrows trained several miles to the south. My GPS took me through a myriad of country lanes to what had a clearly been a farm house. Two rows of brick built boxes – or rather one of brick and the second, seemingly built some time previously, of brick and wood combined –adjoined the house with a thick privet hedge and a high dark-brown gate blocking out much of the view from the road. The wooden board said 'Green Hill Stables – Private Property.' I drove slowly past and, when I found somewhere to turn, slowly back again. I caught a glimpse of a few horses but nothing that was obviously Grey Somali.

I drove back the way I had come for half a mile or so, with the narrow road dominated by the hill in front of me. I had a vague recollection of having passed a footpath sign, suggesting it pointed to a way up the hill, on my journey there. Sure enough, there it was by a small lay-by. Plenty of room for the BMW. It looked pretty muddy each side of the style. Lucky I'd brought a pair of boots.

It took me twenty minutes to get to the top and around the side, after disturbing half a dozen sheep who took fright at my appearance and noisily sought safety elsewhere. Hopefully the farmer wasn't watching. I found myself with a distant view of the stables and the house but I was too far away to make out much detail. A bit further round, though, the view was much more interesting. A gallop, with wooden railings, was clearly visible. It must have been about six furlongs round with a straight piece extending at the far corner. Alongside the straight section was a line of schooling fences. Next time I would bring binoculars and I would come a lot earlier.

An hour later I was back at my desk, mapping the Alec Smith article – writing out a summary and putting in where the various quotes should go. I then only needed to decide on an opening sentence that would catch the reader's attention, and I could start typing. The secret of a good article, I'd long since found, was to get all your ducks in a row and then your words could flow without interruption.

A cup of coffee first. But my mind was never far away from Emma. I had to really force myself to concentrate on the possible star of the Hilton.

Stuart and Belinda lived in a white-painted four-bedroom two storey fronted by a large lawn in one of Reading's secluded suburbs, quite a change from the three-bedroom semi they bought early in their married life. After our parents died of Covid-19 in the same week just over two years ago Belinda bought the house with her share of the inheritance, but she had never quite got over being unable to visit them when they had fallen sick or after they were rushed to hospital on successive days.

She opened the front door as I pulled up outside it – I'd rung to tell her I wanted her help with something without saying what – and kissed me affectionately on both cheeks when I reached her. 'Come on in. It's all quiet now – the twins are in school until half twelve.'

She led the way, in jeans and a pale blue jersey, into a kitchen warmed by what I regarded as an Aga but was probably something much more modern. Belinda had made sure there was enough money left to fit out the house with everything the present-day housewife wants. 'Coffee?'

I sat down at the table while she switched on the espresso machine and put mugs and sugar on the table. She nattered about the twins, the weather and the government while the coffee was being made and I hardly got a word in until she poured the hot froth into the mugs and took the seat opposite me, pushing the sugar bowl in my direction.

'So what's the big problem?' She smiled encouragingly. I suddenly had an uneasy feeling she already knew.

'Well I got kicked on the arm at Sandown on Friday.' I found myself rubbing it in some sort of involuntary reflex action. 'I went to casualty but it was packed with the injured from some dreadful accident on the M4 so I waited until I could see Stuart on Saturday morning.'

'I heard. A crack, four weeks no riding. Sorry,' she realised I hadn't finished. 'Carry on.'

'Well, the dragon wasn't there. There was a new receptionist called Emma.'

'Ah,' she grinned. "I might have known my brother would fall for the lovely blonde.'

I tried desperately, and unsuccessfully, to stop myself going red. Belinda grinned again. 'So, how can I help?'

'Well......' I had to go through with this. It was the reason I was here, embarrassingly baring my soul to my big sister. At least that's how it felt. 'The thing is she's not there anymore and I don't know how to contact her. I don't even know her surname.'

'So you want me to find out for you?' She was turning the screw, and she knew it.

'Yes. Got it in one.'

'And what are you offering in return?' She was smiling broadly, revelling in my discomfiture.

'What do you mean? What do you want?'

She laughed. 'Nothing, you fool. I'm only pulling your leg. Course I'll help. Did you try the agency?'

'I don't know what it's called.'

'It'll be the Medical Staff Agency, the Reading office. That's the one the practice normally uses. Hang on, I'll get the number.'

She disappeared through the kitchen door into the room she and Stuart used as a home office. Two minutes later she was back holding a small piece of paper. 'This is it.'

'Great, thanks a lot Belinda.'

'Not yet. It won't do you any good. They're not going to give out a staff member's number to just anyone who rings up and wants to know.'

'I suppose you're right.' My uplifted spirits took a sharp dive.

'Let's see what I can do.' She reached for her handbag on the sideboard, fished out a phone and started dialling.

'Good morning. It's Belinda Richardson, Stuart's wife, New Street Surgery. Could I speak to Marjorie?'

There was a lengthy pause. 'She's in anyway..... Ah Marjorie, how are you?' The conversation turned from health to the weather to some joint acquaintance's abrupt manner. 'Typical, she's always like that. It's time she learned some manners.

'Marjorie, I'll tell you why I'm ringing. Emma was with us for the last fortnight....Yes, super girl, she's so good with the patients, with the doctors too - and that's even more important. The thing is Marjorie, when I was cleaning out the desk ready for Eliza's return, I found a purse in the drawer. No money in it or anything but it's quite a nice purse and it might be hers... No, don't you worry, just give me the number and I'll ring her... I would like to thank her anyway, she did go out of her way to help us ..... Sure, I'll hold.'

She gave me a wink. 'Yes, still here.' She wrote down the number and read it back. 'And what's her surname did you say? ...Thanks a lot, Marjorie. Lovely to talk to you again ... and you.'

'Here we are - Emma Johnson. Now all I need is a detailed description of how the first date goes and we're quits.'

I laughed, gratefully, and finally relaxed. I was fond of my sister, and not just because she treated me like the kid brother of our childhood. We'd always had a lot in common, despite the five years between us, and the tragic death of our parents somehow seemed to have brought us even closer.

On the way back to Kennet Walk I debated whether,

or rather when, to ring Emma. She was probably in some other surgery full of patients and doctors, all expecting 100% concentration on the job. They would take a poor view of the temporary receptionist taking private phone calls. Obviously it would be better to wait until around 6.00pm.

Concentrating on Alec Smith proved difficult. I kept thinking about how I was going to word my invitation to Emma; I would only get one chance and probably only a couple of minutes. If I fluffed it, that would be the end. Three times I started the article but I knew it was crap. I went for a walk round the block but I still couldn't concentrate.

To hell with what the doctors and patients thought. I picked up my mobile and dialled. But supposing she didn't answer? It rang – at least she hadn't got it switched off – but there was no answer. It didn't even go to voicemail. Just when I was about to give up …'Hello.' The voice was little more than a whisper.

'Hi Emma. It's Rod Hutchinson. We met when I came to the surgery on Saturday.'

There was a horribly long pause. 'Oh …. Rodney? …. the jockey?....with the arm?'

'That's the one. How are you?'

'Busy… but how are you? And how's the arm?'

This was more like it. After a few pleasantries I asked her if she would like to come out for a meal one evening.

'Love to. When were you thinking of?'

'Saturday?'

'Sorry, can't do Saturday. But Sunday would be fine. Or Friday.'

We settled on Sunday. She gave me instructions to her flat and, voice dropping, said: 'Got to go now, Rod. See you Sunday.'

I was too excited to concentrate on the article. I went for a second walk round the block, this time feeling on top of the world. Hell, I could finish Alec Smith later, do Robbie Bolton tomorrow and the Grahams on Thursday.

But on the walk I remembered something. I took my phone out of my trouser pocket, looked up the number and dialled. 'John, Rod Hutchinson…Yes, fine …. and you? Listen John, Grey Somali, Sandown last Friday. Did you get the sample results yet?'

There was a pause while John Jameson, the British Horseracing Authority's chief press officer, looked up the relevant page on his computer. 'I don't think anything showed up, Rod. I'd have heard about if there was a positive. Ah, here we are. All tests completed, sample clear.'

'OK thanks.'

'Why Rod? Did you hear anything different?' Jameson used to be a journalist. Clearly his mind still worked the same way, despite his having moved into the establishment. The last thing I wanted was him sounding out whether or not I had a story.

'No. Just somebody said something. You know how it is. You have to check these things. Just in case.'

'Of course. I presume you'll be at the Hilton on Saturday?'

'Doubt it. The Major 'll be covering that. Chances are I'll be at Haydock.'

'Lucky you.'

I said goodbye and disconnected, my mind working overtime. In addition to testing every winner, and the placed horses as well in big races, the BHA's eagle-eyed officials also ordered a test on any horse that looked suspicious. Occasionally something showed up and, when it did, the authorities came down on the unfortunate trainer like the proverbial ton of bricks.

But the rare occasions when the dopers managed to get one step ahead of the BHA chemists - and come up with a substance not covered by the tests - were the sort of things racing journalists dream about. There were few bigger stories.

Was Oliver Chester-Beatty wrong? Or had I stumbled on dynamite?

4

Haydock on Saturday was cold and wet, with fog threatening to close in throughout the final twenty miles of the M6. The press room was empty except for a couple of Northern stalwarts well wrapped up in padded jackets, scarves and flat caps. 'Thought you would be at Sandown,' greeted the younger of the pair while the other man just nodded.

The Major, as expected, had opted for the Hilton Chase fixture. I'd suggested to Brett that I should drive north as Haydock was clearly the second best of the day's four other meetings.

'Heard you broke your arm in that Sandown fall,' continued the more talkative scribe. "Obviously I was told wrong.'

'Cracked it,' I replied, pointing to my left forearm with the index finger of my right hand. 'Luckily my brother-in-law is a doctor. He put the arm in a sort of plastic splint. He x-rayed it again yesterday and said I should be OK to resume in three weeks.' What Stuart actually said was: 'Come back again in a fortnight and we'll have another look at it. But for God's sake, no riding in the meantime. Any pressure and the crack could easily spread.'

The Hilton was the main race at Haydock too with the sparse crowd gathering round the televisions in the restaurant and the various bars. Even some of the bookmakers deserted their posts for the race. In the straight the increasing murmurs from the crowd were drowned out by shouts of 'Go on Robbie' ... 'Go get him Bolton' as Mandable moved up to challenge Gallant George between the last two fences. But sitting only two lengths behind, and going by far the best, was Big Thomas. It looked like Chester-Beatty was going to be proved right.

His horse was only a length off the other two as he jumped the last, ears pricked, but on landing he stumbled. His jockey sat tight. The horse gamely battled to regain his footing but one of those behind galloped straight into him and both horses fell, bringing down two more. Gallant George maintained a half-length advantage over Mandable all the way to the line where young Alec Smith stood up in the stirrups and saluted the cheering crowd. Ploughing on up the hill to take third, five lengths back, was the Grahams' horse Canada Dry. I was thrilled for them.

An hour or so later, after speaking to jockeys – beaten ones as well as the winners – throughout the afternoon, plus trainers and bookmakers, I'd cobbled together what I considered an interesting report. I was just waiting for the last race before filing. I wanted to get away as soon as I could because the fog had become a lot worse, and the journey down south looked like being a tough one.

'There's a lot of money for High Ransom,' remarked the elder Northern scribe as the three of us sat in front of the big press room TV. 'Backed from 33-1 to 4-1. No form worth speaking of - six bloody noughts behind it's name.'

I looked at the fourteen runners for the Newton-le-Willows Handicap Hurdle in my racecard. High Ransom, a seven-year-old gelding, had not won a race for three years. I'd hardly heard of the trainer but my curiosity was aroused when I saw the horse was ridden by Harry Jones.

Visibility was poor for much of the race but I could see that Jones had settled his mount in mid-division. As the stands' camera picked up the field out of the fog halfway up the straight he was still in much the same position but, almost immediately after jumping the second last, High Ransom found another gear and he was in front as he reached the final flight. He jumped it smoothly and won comfortably.

'Bugger me,' muttered the younger of my two colleagues as he packed up his laptop case before heading out to the car park.

I went to the winner's enclosure and got there as Harry Jones rode in, touching his cap out of habit – there was hardly anybody there to cheer in the gathering gloom, spoke briefly to the man I assumed to be the trainer, Tom Swarter, as he unbuckled the girth and went off with his saddle to weigh in.

But what attracted my attention was the horse. High Ransom lashed out with his aluminium-tipped hind hooves as Jones took the saddle off, and again when the jockey went behind him en route to the clerk of the scales. Although the stable lad took hold of his head, and made calming noises as he led the chestnut gelding round the small arena, the horse snorted repeatedly, kept tossing his head and his eyes were popping. He looked as if something had frightened the daylights out of him. Tom Swarter went up to the lad, said something I didn't catch and the horse was led out of the ring in the direction of the stables with Swarter following a couple of yards behind.

I was just setting off in pursuit when a voice beside me said: 'Rodney, I must congratulate you on your articles. You really convey the atmosphere and the excitement of the racecourse.' The speaker was a man in his sixties, tall with a trilby and a knee-length Barbour. I wanted to get after Swarter before he disappeared but you can't ignore the public. A racing journalist needs his readers as much as an MP needs his constituents. When they read your articles, day after day, they feel they know you almost as a friend and I was a firm believer in mingling with the crowds; many of them liked to talk, often giving you snippets of information that they think might be useful. It was only when the conversationalist started reminiscing about his own riding days that I felt I could make my excuses.

I went straight to the stables. My path was blocked by the security guard on the gate. I said who I was and stressed that I needed to speak to the trainer of the last race winner. 'Sorry sir. Only trainers and stable staff with permits allowed through 'ere.'

'Excuse me.' A girl wearing waterproofs and carrying a bucket squeezed between me and the guard.

'Hey. Can you help? I need to speak to Tom Swarter and I'm not allowed in. Could you ask him to come here?'

'Sure, his horses are next to ours. I'll get him now.'

Less than two minutes later she was back. 'Sorry. He'd already gone. His horses are still here, though. They're washing down the last winner and then they'll load up.'

I thanked her and hurried back to the weighing room. The guard on the jockeys' room door had already left - fortunately for me – and, passing three valets sorting piles of dirty white breeches and mud-spattered colours, I found Harry Jones sitting on a bench at the far end putting on his shoes.

'Harry, well done. Were you always travelling like a winner? We couldn't see much with the fog.'

The jockey's opposition to me at Sandown eight days earlier had disappeared, perhaps in the elation of success. Or because this time I was not in opposition. 'Ah, Mister 'Utchinson, good to see you.' He stood up and reached out a hand to shake mine. 'Aye, 'e was well 'andicapped.' The Welsh accent, and its melodic lilt, seemed even more pronounced than before. 'We expected 'im to win and I never 'ad a moment's doubt.'

'He seemed very excited in the winner's enclosure. His eyes were popping out of his head.'

'So would yours be if you'd finally won after all those races.' He laughed at his own joke. 'I don't think e'd won for sum't like three years.'

Next on my list were the stewards. I knocked on the door of their sanctum and went straight in. The only person left in the oak-panelled room was Lawrence Matthews sitting at the long table, a sea of papers in front of him and a tea tray with a patterned pot and matching cup and saucer at his elbow.

He looked up and glared at me. 'Sorry Lawrence. Was

there any inquiry in the last? Into the winner's improved form?'

'Why? Nobody fell off this time.'

I could see this was going to be difficult, but I wasn't going to let him get away with that. 'Well, for a start he hadn't won a race for three years, he had a string of noughts in front of his name and he was backed almost off the board. Surely you couldn't have ignored that?'

Lawrence Matthews took his glasses off and replied testily. 'Of course we didn't but I would remind you that this was a handicap with all runners having a theoretical equal chance. Also this was his proper distance – his previous two runs this season were over only two miles. But maybe you hadn't noticed. Also the ground today was heavy, the same as when he last won.'

'And the betting? Didn't that suggest he was off in a big way, and that he might not have been in those two earlier races this season? And he was so stirred up his eyes were coming out of his head.'

'Mr Hutchinson.' There was a long pause, his gaze never leaving my face. 'I'm sure your readers will be interested in your observations. But the stewards cannot make libellous accusations in our reports – we would be in trouble if we did, and rightly so. We have to be fair to all concerned.'

'So there was no inquiry?'

'No – and, as I keep trying to make it clear to you, there was not sufficient justification to hold one.'

'OK. Thanks.' It was as much as I could do not to slam the door behind me. I hurried out towards the bookmakers' ring. Even before I got there I could see it was empty. But there were still lights in the nearby reserved car park and I saw what looked like a bookmaker's board being loaded into the back of a Toyota Rav. As I got near I saw it belonged to one of the bookies I'd been speaking to earlier.

'Hi,' I began. 'Was there a lot of money on the last winner?'

'A lot of money? It poured on like there was no tomorrow. They'd been hooking that thing for two years. Hardly surprising it absolutely pissed in.'

The speaker, his assistant already in the passenger seat, took off his pork pie hat and tossed it into the back of the Rav on top of the board which read 'Jack Joseph - Best prices since 1995.'

'Did you lose much?'

'Nah. It was an online job and we saw it coming. Made a few quid out of it actually. Knew it must be worth a bet if there was all that much already on. You writing about it?'

I told him about there being no inquiry. 'Typical. Last race, all they're thinking about is getting off home.' He got into his car and grinned. 'I'll look forward to reading your report.'

Back in the now-empty press room, I debated what to do. It was surely the story so far as Haydock was concerned, and the rest of the media would almost certainly have missed it. I was sure those two other journalists wouldn't have spoken to Jack Joseph, or Lawrence Matthews for that matter. They too were keen to get home. But I needed more time. I had to get hold of Tom Swarter, and Brett would already be agitating.

I decided to add only a couple of paragraphs about the gamble of the day and ten minutes later, after filing and checking with Brett that he had the copy, I was on my way south.

The fog was even worse than I feared. It took me half an hour to cover the first fifteen miles and, when the Knutsford Services sign loomed up, I greeted it like a Bedouin spotting an oasis in a sandstorm. The place was packed with noisy football supporters and, after settling for a burger and chips – Belinda would have given me a lecture on nutrition – and a Coca Cola to keep me awake on the rest of the journey, I searched for somewhere to sit. Every table was taken but maybe there was a spare chair. I heard somebody shouting 'Rodney' and saw a man waving his hat. It was Jack Joseph with his pork pie. I hadn't realised that, without it, he was bald bar a few strands of hair brushed across his scalp.

He introduced me to his assistant, a man in his early twenties who said his name was Arnold and added that he was Jack's nephew. 'Arsenal were playing United,' he said in a broad Birmingham accent, pointing to the sea of people around us. 'It was a draw, two all,' he added. It was one of his few contributions to the conversation.

Jack, whose Brum accent was much less pronounced, hardly stopped talking. He promptly offered his own views on football: 'Plymouth Argyll supporter meself, not that it's ever done me much good'; the government: 'Always voted Tory but I do wonder sometimes'; the weather; 'This fuckin' fog 'll be the death of me. Arnold says it's clear by Stoke – thank God.'

Between mouthfuls of my meal I asked him what he meant by High Ransom being an online job. 'It's the modern version of those old betting shop coups - you know, getting an army of people to put on £50 each in a whole lot of different shops all at the same time.'

I nodded as I sipped my coke. I knew exactly what he meant. Some of those coups had gone down in folklore.

'All you need these days is a whole lot of laptops,' Jack continued. 'One man can have ten set up. He opens accounts with different bookmakers beforehand, maybe puts a tenner on a couple of horses to get the accounts operating and avert any suspicion. On the day of the coup, say twenty minutes before the race – maybe ten - he has the laptops opened at the account page of each bookmaker with a £100 stake entered. When he thinks the time is right, he presses Accept on one laptop after the other. Can place ten bets inside thirty seconds - twenty inside a minute if he's got enough laptops. That's £20,000 he's got on before the layers get wind of what's going on and get a chance to slash the price.'

I listened, fascinated. It was going to make an interesting article. I said as much.

'I hope you're going to write about weRthebestbets too. They need exposing.' Jack Joseph was referring to the latest star on the betting firmament. A relatively new company – few people had heard of them a year ago – *weRthebestbets. com* were rattling the cages of the big established firms by offering better prices and eye-catching invitations to open accounts.

Nobody seemed to know who was behind the company but it had the advantage of low overheads – it operated only online and had no betting shops or on-course presence. It was also a big advertiser with *sports-all.com*.

'Exposing? How do you mean?' I wasn't aware of them doing anything underhand. If anything, the opposite. They were sponsoring an increasing number of races.

'Insider trading for starters.' Joseph looked up as at least half the tables in the restaurant began to empty. 'The Arsenal coaches are leaving,' Arnold explained. His uncle, treating the mass exodus as an irrelevance, continued: 'They give trainers over the odds and then ask them for information about how certain horses have been working.' Warming to his theme, he picked up a knife and banged the handle down onto the table. 'When big-race fancied horses meet with a setback, they give the trainers their money back and then ask to be kept informed about other horses in the stable. All the while Joe Punter is kept in the dark.'

I couldn't see where the crime was. The major bookmakers all had high profile PR men who made a point of keeping close to trainers, big-name owners and leading members of the media. If any of these wanted a favour, such as a point or two over the odds, I was pretty sure they would get it. I said as much to Jack Joseph.

'There you are, you see.' He raised his voice and banged the knife handle down a second time. 'You're all in it together. One rule for the ordinary Joe and the likes of me, and another for all the toffs.'

He was getting red in the face, dangerously so. 'You're missing the point. They don't just give trainers their money back. They milk the punters - and the other bookmakers – with the information. Often they keep quiet for days, increase the price to attract money for a horse they know is not going to run, and back other fancied horses in the race. When word does break that the favourite has gone wrong, the odds of the other runners tumble – and they are already on at big prices, using money they've obtained under false pretences.'

'I see,' I said slowly, as I digested what he had said. 'I didn't know about any of that.'

Joseph wasn't finished. 'You heard about Lazarus Luke?' I nodded. 'He'd been injured for the best part of a fortnight when Chester-Beatty let on to some journalist that there was a big doubt about him for the Guineas.'

'Not some journalist, Jack. Me.'

'And why didn't you say something about why he hadn't made it public when the horse got hurt? That's what I mean. You're all involved. I suppose you were backing some of the others in the race yourself?'

Joseph's complexion had gone from red to puce, and every fibre in his body was as tense as a wound-up spring. 'Listen Jack. I spoke to Oliver Chester-Beatty when I was asking him about Big Thomas in the Hilton Chase over a week ago. And I asked him how Lazarus Luke was progressing, just because the horse is news and I'm a journalist. He told me about the swelling in the horse's hind leg and that it wouldn't go down. Therefore he had it scanned. Only then did he know that the horse would have to be on the easy list for a couple of months. I'm quite sure he had no intention of deceiving anybody.'

'Huh.' Joseph was clearly unconvinced but I changed the subject to the Hilton Chase and the melee at the final fence. Luckily the bookmaker had made good money on the race and his heart-attack complexion returned to something nearer normal as he relived the finish. Arnold, who had said nothing since his comment about the Arsenal coaches leaving, took advantage of the calmer atmosphere, and got to his feet. 'Time we hit the road,' he informed his uncle.

I shook hands with both of them, said I would look forward to seeing them again in the near future - and I meant it. The bookmaker was clearly passionate about his way of life and something of a character.

I ran through what he had said about *weRthebestbets.com* when I got back on the motorway but as the fog lifted – Arnold was right about Stoke. Indeed it cleared about five miles before the Newcastle-under-Lyme and Stoke-on-Trent exit– my thoughts drifted towards Emma. I'd been trying not to think about her, and by now she would be out with the boyfriend. Don't be ridiculous, I told myself. Stupid to feel jealous. After all I hardly knew her. We'd only had two short conversations in the surgery and a third over the phone. In any case tonight's date couldn't be that serious. She would never have agreed to go out with me if it had been. All the same, I worried.

I tried to think of other things and, by the time I reached the M40, I had also thought through the reasons why Lawrence Matthews disliked me so much. True, he seemed to have it in for a lot of people. That quip about a chip on both shoulders was pretty near the mark, and he gave the impression of being a bit of a pocket Hitler whenever he got the chance. But with me I suspected it was my public school accent. I'd come across a few people who seemed to resent me because of it, even though mine wasn't in any way pronounced. Some people, I knew, tried to disguise it by adopting a local accent but I was damned if I was going to do that. It would be akin to betraying my upbringing and my parents, to say nothing of all the money they had spent on trying to do what they believed to be the best for their children.

But the Grey Somali-High Ransom cases had me puzzled. The similarities were too obvious to be coincidence. Both returning to form when heavily backed, plus – and this was really the point – both behaving like startled rabbits caught in the headlights. Could this be the dopers' Holy Grail? Somehow I had to find out.

I waited until just after 10.00am on Sunday before ringing Tom Swarter on his mobile. I needed to get him after he had finished any morning work with the horses and, in the unlikely event of his being a churchgoer, before he left home. He answered on the third ring.

I said who I was and congratulated him on High Ransom's win to get him in a friendly frame of mind. 'He hadn't won for quite some time. Had he had problems in the last two seasons?'

'Well, I suppose he'd had a few,' came the hesitant reply. 'You don't get many seven-year-old jumpers that don't, you know. But nothing that serious. Saturday's race was made for him. Right distance – he stays longer than the mother-in-law –and the ground was bottomless.'

'Sure,' I wanted him to think I was accepting as fact everything he was telling me so that he wouldn't suspect I believed otherwise. And I needed to keep him talking to get material for my article. 'Did you back him, Tom? There seemed to be plenty of money for him.'

'Ah, just a few quid to cover the expenses, you know.'

'The price shortened from 20-1 to 4-1. Must have covered a fair few expenses.' I laughed to take away any insinuations he might read into my comment.

'Ah well, the owner likes a punt, you know. And he likes to tell his friends.' I'd already looked up the owner. There was no mention of George Rickards in the *Directory of the Turf* and those on Facebook and Google made no mention of any connection with racehorses.

'I'll give him a ring, Tom. What's his number?'

'Mmm.' There was a long pause. 'I dunno about that. He hates publicity and he would be annoyed if I started giving it to people. Don't say I said so but Weatherbys 'll give it to you.'

'Thanks Tom – and well done again.'

I was pretty sure the British Horseracing Authority's secretariat wouldn't give it to me. In any case I suspected that it was Tom Swarter himself who had both engineered the return to form and organised the gamble; obviously the owner had to be in the know but that was probably as far as it went.

I looked up the trainer's address in the *Horses In Training* book and Googled the map. He lived about four miles from where Grey Somali was trained. Four miles is nothing for a racehorse.

The article almost wrote itself. No need for any mapping with this one. I began with all the money coming for a horse with no form, and I used most of the Jack Joseph's car park quotes including 'Poured on like there was no tomorrow… It absolutely p***** in'….. But I left out the highly libellous 'they'd been hooking that thing for two years.' I attributed the comments to 'a prominent course bookmaker' rather than mentioning Joseph by name. That way nobody (Joseph included) could complain.

But I did quote Tom Swarter, Harry Jones and Lawrence Matthews. I knew Matthews wouldn't like it but he didn't deserve any favours from me. I made no mention of Grey Somali – people might think it sour grapes as he had caused me to fall – or the fact that the horses were trained quite near to each other.

However at the end I wrote: 'One of the most curious aspects of the coup – and legitimate excuses for the horse's return to form there undoubtedly are – is the state of the winner after the race. You might have expected a horse that had just slogged through two and three-quarter miles of heavy Haydock to be tired to the point of exhaustion. Not High Ransom. He positively danced around the winner's enclosure, lashing out in all directions, and his eyes were popping out of his head as if he had seen a ghost.'

Two hours later, going through the various online racing websites to make sure I was up to date with all the news, I saw that my article – headed 'Had Gambled-on Winner Seen A Ghost?' - attracted more than 20 comments.

These comments were one of the biggest selling points of *sports-all.com*. They appeared directly below the articles and were as popular with readers as the articles themselves. Brett used them to sell the website to advertisers but they were a lot of work and kept Tony and Michelle, his two editorial assistants, in full time employment. The readers' views and opinions had to be read carefully before being published with anything considered libellous, or obviously inaccurate, being deleted.

5

'Do you bring all your girlfriends here?' Emma's question, delivered with a broad smile, was clearly intended to tease but it was uncomfortably close to the truth – not that I'd had as many as her words seemed to imply, certainly not as many as I would have liked.

Part of the appeal of The Riverside Arms at Pangbourne was its close proximity to the Thames, although it's popularity was due to much more than that. The whole of one wall was taken up by the long bar and much of the rest of the pub was given over to the open-plan restaurant. Many of the tables were in their own individual alcoves. There was a four-piece band at weekends when the place was invariably packed.

I'd booked a table and Seamus, the proprietor, greeted me like an old friend as he ushered us to one of the alcove tables. It wasn't so much that I was a valued customer but because he was a racing fanatic. He took Emma's pink coat, said he would hang it up somewhere safe and asked what we would like to drink. She asked for a gin and tonic while I had a brandy and ginger ale.

She looked fabulous with her blonde hair offsetting a pale blue jersey, a skirt in darker blue and black stockings. I said 'wow' when I picked her up and in the pub I again told her she looked stunning. She seemed to appreciate both the compliment and the surroundings. The band started up, adding to the atmosphere but without drowning out our conversation.

As the evening wore on, and over the meal, she seemed as keen to find out about me as I was about her. I learned that she had spent most of her life in the Reading area where her father was a vet – no horses but a partner in a busy small animal clinic - and that she had drifted into medical reception almost by accident. Not knowing what she wanted to do when she left school, she broke off a cookery course (which she hated) to help out when the receptionist at her own doctor's surgery fell ill. She loved it and, after a year or so, found the experience was a passport to international travel. So far she had had jobs in Philadelphia, Melbourne and Austria. She was planning to go back to America in the spring. Her mother was American so the Green Card was no great problem.

She learned that my family was from Worcester where the Hutchinson & Hutchinson firm of solicitors had been in practice for nearly a century. I was to have been the fourth- generation partner, joining my father, my uncle and a second cousin when Covid-19 wiped out both parents. I was just six months away from my finals and, in a week of sad reflection, I decided on a wholesale change of direction.

I'd become hooked on racing soon after starting riding in my last year at Malvern College, and I progressed to point-to-points a couple of years later when studying law at Warwick University. Soon I was also writing reports on the meetings for the local papers and, when *sports-all.com* started up, I sent them reports too. Brett welcomed these but told me it was the copy on the races in which I was riding that really caught his attention and, when I progressed to the racecourse proper, he published those too.

I determined to give up the law once I qualified, splash part of my inheritance on buying a couple of racehorses and keeping them in training. I didn't give Emma the financial details – it didn't seem right somehow - but the house at Severn Stoke was worth the best part of half a million and my father's share of the firm another £100,000. I told Brett what I was doing and asked for a contract as a full time racing journalist. He agreed but paid me rather less than half the £140 a day that the horses were costing me.

Our respective life stories were just about at an end as the same time as the meal when Seamus came up and asked how we liked it. I felt thrilled when Emma said 'It was lovely – and I must thank my companion for bringing me to such a delightful place.'

Seamus bowed in her direction – 'the pleasure is mine, my dear.' Turning to me, he said he had backed Brown River – 'That Grey Somali horse should have been disqualified. The jockey rode him straight into you.'

'Was that when you cracked your arm?' asked Emma.

'You cracked your arm?' Seamus made it sound as if Harry Jones had committed a criminal offence. 'Does that mean you are going to be out of action?'

'Only for another three weeks. Could have been a lot worse.'

'I want to back Brown River next time,' Seamus seemed as if he meant business. 'He'll be a good thing.'

After he had gone to pay his respects to more of his customers, Emma asked me about the jockey who rode into me and why no action had been taken against him. I explained as best I could, and told her about Grey Somali's behaviour in the winner's enclosure and that of High Ransom at Haydock.

'Are you saying they were given some sort of stimulant to make them win?'

'I think they might have been, although the British Horseracing Authority people will tell you that's not possible without it showing up.' I explained about the dope tests on every winner and told her of the widespread belief that some of the dopers might still be a step ahead of the racing ruling body. I also told her what I had written in that morning's report on the website.

'My God,' she sounded worried. "Won't the people who did the doping try to attack you to stop you writing anything else - or at least frighten you off?'

'I suppose it's possible." I said slowly, thinking about what she had said. 'But you can't just chicken out. You have to write what you believe and what you believe should be written. If you cherry-pick your stories, or your subject matter, you shouldn't be a journalist in the first place.'

She reached for my hand and squeezed it. A surge of pain shot through my left forearm like an electric shock. 'Oh Rod, I'm so sorry. I should have known.'

I smiled. Her concern delighted me even more than the pain had hurt me. We carried on talking for the best part of an hour before she looked at her watch and said it was time we went. She was starting a new assignment in the morning, and she needed to be there by 8.30am.

After bidding farewell to Seamus - 'Rod's going to win on Brown River next time' he informed everyone within earshot - we drove back to the house where she lived near Tilehurst. It was a big three-storey Georgian affair in its own grounds and divided into eight flats, with the elderly couple who owned it living - off the rents - on the ground floor.

Emma said she wasn't going to invite me in, much to my disappointment. It was already late and she had to be up early, but her lingering goodnight kiss left me hoping that just maybe she felt the same way about me as I did about her.

The *Racing Post* reproduced my 'Gambled-on Winner' story in Monday's paper. The *Post*, required reading for everyone in racing, occasionally published articles that had impressed its editorial staff after appearing elsewhere but this was the first time they had given VIP treatment to one of mine. I didn't receive any payment but the kudos was considerable. People would take note of the name Rod Hutchinson, not least other journalists and their editors - even though Tom Swarter would probably be splitting blood, if not actually gunning for me. At the very least he was going to be doubly careful about that he said to me in future.

The next big story was *weRthebestbets.com*. I knew my way around the Companies House website from my days as an articled clerk but repeated searches revealed disappointingly little, and seemingly that was the intention; *weRthebestbets. com* was a registered trading name belonging to a company called Jones Williams Smith Ltd whose shareholders were all limited companies. These, in turn, were all owned by other companies whose names gave little indication of what they did or the people behind them. When I researched them I found that every single one was owned by other companies, all with similarly anonymous names.

I could have gone on all day but I didn't have the patience. I decided to try another tack. His number wasn't in my phone but I knew I had an ancient address book somewhere in my father's old desk, the one he used at home - a Queen Anne antique he was so proud of that I decided to take it out of the auction when Belinda and I sold off the house contents.

George Goodbody, tall, good-looking and charming – well-named according to many of the girls on the Warwick campus who referred to him as Gorgeous George - was working his way towards his fortune in a City merchant bank. If anybody could find out, he could. Fortunately he still had the same mobile number.

I explained what I was looking for and the brick wall I'd come up against at Companies House. 'So you want me to make inquiries?' he responded, almost before I'd finished my explanation. 'No problem. Can you give me a day or two? Things are a bit hectic here at the moment. Trying to raise millions for some takeover bid.'

'Sure. Won't hold you up now George.'

'Before you go, Rod, when's your next winner?' Like far too many people I came across, George was convinced that racing is fixed and that making money out of it is largely a matter of knowing the right trainers and jockeys. I explained about the crack in my arm keeping me out of action for the next three weeks. But I told him I had high hopes that Brown River would provide compensation next time. He should ignore Ezekiel's next race as he would only be having a run to get him ready for my return.

'Ezekiel, that sounds interesting,' He spoke much more slowly this time, as if he was making a mental note of the name. 'I'll be back to you before the end of the week. Maybe you'll then have some idea of the date of his race when you're back riding him. I wouldn't want to miss that.'

I shuddered. The likes of George Goodbody tended to take tentative tips as gospel, and bet accordingly. When they lost, I suffered terrible feelings of guilt.

John Jameson was ready for me when I rang on Tuesday morning – I had thought of checking with him the previous day; other scribes would have read my piece in the *Post* but I was pretty sure the results would not have been finally processed by then. All the same, I didn't want anybody stealing a march on me.

'Morning Rod. You want to know about High Ransom?' The BHA's chief press officer sounded ominously cheerful. 'I asked for his sample to be given priority after reading your piece. Negative for every test – and I asked them to check the B sample just to make sure.'

I knew all urine samples were divided into two just in case the first one was lost, spilt or met with some other mishap. Once in South Africa the samples from the biggest race meeting of the year were stolen. The theft made headlines round the world.

'So there must have been some other reason for the horse dancing round like a cat on hot bricks with his eyes popping out?' I knew I sounded dubious. I was.

'Probably just excitement. Or reaction from being given a hard race. It happens you know, Rod.'

'Yes...either that or they used something your people haven't found yet.'

'Rod, not that old chestnut, please.' Jameson was clearly irritated.

'It's not an old chestnut, John. The dopers have often been one step ahead of the BHA and Jockey Club chemists over the years.... As you well know.'

'OK Rod. But listen. I really went into this in great detail when I came here. I had to because I thought the same as you,' Jameson's tone left little doubt that he believed what he was saying, and that he wasn't simply repeating the party line. 'I spent days with the chemists, and I spoke to the authorities in the States, France, Ireland and other places. We have really got to grips. Our tests now are vastly better than they were, they cover every possible stimulant and are just about fool proof.'

'You would say that, wouldn't you? As Mandy Rice-Davies might have said.' I laughed at my own joke.

Jameson was not amused. 'Rod, one thing I would ask: whatever you're going to write, please do not say anything that is going to give racing a bad name. We have enough trouble trying to counter all the ill-informed, derogatory bilge on social media without highly-regarded journalists like yourself making unproven suggestions.'

The compliment was deliberate. Jameson knew just how

pressmen's minds work, having been one himself. But I felt a warm glow all the same.

'Sure John – and I'll be careful what I say.'

I was. My article reported that the sample from Saturday's heavily-backed winner High Ransom had proved negative, and quoted Jameson about the present-day tests being much improved and just about fool proof. But I also wrote about the dopers using substances that sometimes hadn't shown up in the past. I sent it in with a note to Brett to go carefully with the headline. I suggested 'Heavily-backed High Ransom not doped.' Eye-catching but true, and not something that could make Jameson shirty next time I needed to speak to him.

Tom Swarter, though, would be furious – for the second time inside three days. I thought back to Emma's words on Sunday evening. Would he really attack me? Or, more likely, pay someone to do it for him? An unnerving shiver ran up my spine.

His yard was quite different from that of Bob Arrows. For a start it was purpose-built. Two lines of boxes, the stables back and front. I calculated that there would be enough room for forty horses although about a third of the boxes seemed to be empty.

Dusk was threatening to close in by the time I got there shortly after 4.00pm. Half a dozen lads were busily filling hay nets, and taking buckets of horse feed, to the occupant of each box. Judging by the noise when the feed was tipped into the mangers Tom Swarter, like most trainers, preferred the manufactured stuff to mixing up his own natural feed.

From what I could see the horses looked well on it.

The trainer's modern bungalow was at the back and at the front, beside an electric-powered sliding gate, was a white notice board with black lettering saying: 'Hillside Racing Stables. Proprietor Tom Swarter. Visitors by appointment.' At the bottom in small letters were both his landline and his mobile number. The whole place was surrounded by white post-and-rail fencing and the overall impression was of a neat, tidy and professional operation. With my cap pulled down over my eyes I strolled past twice, trying not to show interest. A couple of the lads looked my way but nobody stood and stared, let alone asked me what I was doing. There was no sign of the trainer.

The area was dominated by what I now knew was called Green Hill. Its towering presence was less than half a mile away but, I calculated, on roughly the opposite side from Arrows' stables. I wondered if they both used the same gallop – and the same fright-inducing substance.

It was only just getting light when I pulled into the lay-by and parked as far to the back as I could. Unfortunately the BMW's bright red was going to be visible to anyone driving past. I pulled on my green Puffa over a winter vest, thick shirt and two jerseys. I expected it to be bitterly cold at the top of Green Hill so wore jodhpurs instead of trousers. I pulled on the gum boots and set off with a flask of coffee and my breakfast (two slices of toast).

From the top I could see the stables of both trainers, at a sixty-degree angle. Bob Arrows' string was the first to appear, a dozen of them including one grey horse who I presumed to be Grey Somali. I watched them through my binoculars as they walked towards the wooden railings. When they got there, they circled for about five minutes before a Land Rover drove up and stopped. Arrows, who appeared to be wearing the same navy windcheater he had worn at Sandown, got out and walked towards the horses. I could see his right arm waving and pointing as he gave instructions to the stable lads.

They set off in single file, about five yards apart, at a steady canter and covered all six furlongs of the round gallop before pulling up. Grey Somali, if it was him, was last but one throughout. They circled again while I tried not to move - easier said than done, particularly as the wind had picked up and was painfully cutting through my cold-weather clothing like a butcher's knife. I knew that the Puffa would not be an effective camouflage from down below if I started moving about.

I forced myself to concentrate on the horses. After a few minutes they began to break away from the circle and set off round the gallop a second time, this time in pairs and at a much faster pace. When they reached the far corner they branched off down the straight section and really quickened. Grey Somali, in particular, went very fast indeed with his lad struggling to stop him running away. When he pulled up and rejoined the circle he was sweating profusely and kept prancing around. I couldn't make out his eyes, even with the binocs, but his general appearance matched Oliver Chester-Beatty's Sandown description.

Was he just a highly excitable horse or was whatever they had given him still in his system? My musings were interrupted by the arrival of Tom Swarter's horses followed by the trainer in a Toyota Land Cruiser. This time there were fourteen horses and they circled further away from where the other string – now heading back to their stables – had done.

They followed pretty much the same procedure - cantering round the circuit, one behind the other, before going again at a decent gallop and quickening the tempo when they went on to the final straight. However they did not go as fast, even though a couple of them fought with their riders as they tried to go flat out. These two were also in a state of unnaturally high excitement when they all circled, while Swarter inspected each horse and spoke to their riders one by one.

I wasn't sure whether High Ransom was one of the two playing up; all I remembered from Haydock was that he was a bay and nine of them were that colour. Breakfast and coffee was an increasingly miserable affair as the rain, that had started as Swarter's string headed back towards their stables, intensified and the wind buffeted into something reminiscent of a horror film – at least that's how it seemed as I was totally exposed and rapidly getting soaked through.

There was still the second lot for both trainers to come and I'd set out fully intending to stay for that - and a fair bit longer, just in case one of the two also sent out a horse on its own that they didn't want anyone to see. But I wasn't going to risk catching pneumonia. I passed the sheep of last week as I hurriedly made my way down. There were ten sheltering from the worst of the wind in a hollow but still getting drenched. A couple of them gave a miserable 'baa' at the sight of me but, unlike last week, my appearance didn't frighten them into moving away.

I drove five miles with the heater full on before stopping

to take off most of my wet clothes and, once back in Kennet Walk, I soaked in a hot bath for nearly an hour. I was dozing off when the phone rang. I just managed to reach it without getting out.

'Rod? It's George, George Goodbody.' I was immediately alert.

'Hi George. How's things in the City?'

'Hectic, as usual, but I've got a bit of information for you on that betting company.'

'That's great George. Thanks very much.'

'Well, not really. You're going to have to go to the Caymans to find out the real owners, and the people there won't give anything to anyone.'

'Right, go on.'

The shareholdings are in the name of nominee companies, and this goes back five generations if you know what I mean.'

'Yea, at least I think I do.'

'They trace to two nominee companies registered in the Caymans with addresses care of two legal firms.'

'So, I'm back where I started?

'Yes and no. It's obviously a front and another contact tells me that the company's betting operation is definitely located in the British Isles by people with racing connections – although that last bit is obvious. They wouldn't be betting in such a big way if they didn't know what they were doing, and they'd have to be based in Britain or Ireland I would think. Judging by what they are betting on. I gather they don't take bets on racing elsewhere apart from the big international races like the Arc and the Breeders' Cup.

'True.' I was already wondering how I was going to proceed. I needed more definite information for an article.

'I'll keep asking around – and I'll come back to you when I get something. Any further word on when Ezekiel is going to run?'

'Not yet. But fairly soon, probably in the next fortnight. But I won't be back in time, unfortunately.'

'OK, thanks. I'll take the hint. I never back your horses when you're not riding. I know they're not off.'

'Well,' I hesitated. 'I wouldn't like to say that exactly.' What I actually meant was that I wouldn't like him to go round telling half the City that a racing journalist was deliberately misleading the punters, let alone admitting to an offence as an owner that could see him warned off.

'But you'll be back for Brown River when he returns – and he should win?'

'Yes, hopefully anyway. Don't have too much on, though, George. There are no certainties in racing, as you know.'

A hollow laugh came from the other end. 'You don't have to tell me. I lost ten grand when you fell at Sandown.'

6

'Do you think this is smart enough?' Emma, wearing a red Puffa, tight navy trousers with a scarlet jersey and fashionable black leather boots almost up to her knees, looked sensational when I picked her up at her flat at 10.00am.

Thursday was her day off and she was coming with me to Wincanton. When I'd rung her two days before she asked me what she should wear. A mid-week racemeeting was pretty casual, certainly in November, I'd explained. The important thing was to keep warm.

Brett had rung me on the Monday to make sure I'd be going – just an ordinary length report plus a bit of news. The Major was working from home and wouldn't be racing until Saturday.

There was still an hour before the first when we drove into the press and officials' car park and, setting up the laptop in the press room, I introduced her to the only two other scribes on duty - the *Racing Post* reporter and a Press Association representative - before taking her for an early lunch in the snack bar. She knew, from what I'd said on the phone on Tuesday, that I could be quite busy during the afternoon but she said she didn't mind and would be happy just to watch the horses.

The first race, a maiden hurdle, was won by a complete outsider – a 20-1 chance who had shown nothing in three previous races and who was the pride and joy of his permit holder-trainer. He had also bred the horse and had only two others in his stable just five miles from the course. He was as excited as if he had won the Grand National and he gave me a string of interesting quotes. Back in the press room, I wrote everything down and made a list of people I needed to speak to. In the next hour and a half I found several of them, got much of the news I wanted, wrote the various pieces and filed them.

By this stage I was worried about having left Emma on her own for so long. I found her leaning over the parade ring rails, trying to keep warm and not look too bored as the horses were making their way out onto the course for the next race. 'Sorry Emma, I got delayed. Are you alright?'

She smiled. 'Not dying of cold, not quite anyway. Maybe we could walk round a bit and you can tell me what's what in this world of yours.'

'Come on, we'll go out onto the course and watch from the last fence. This race is a two mile chase so they'll pass us twice.'

The walk towards it seemed to cheer her, mentally as well as physically, and she got quite excited as the thunder of hooves and the bright colours came up the straight towards us. The ground literally shook beneath our feet as the ten runners neared our fence. The horses brushing against the packed birch as they jumped made a loud crashing noise, and at least two of the jockeys shouted something unfathomable. Seconds later they were nothing but a distant memory. All we could see was the battling protagonists heading into the distance as they made their way down the back straight.

'Gosh. That was quite something," she said, grabbing hold of my arm and standing on tiptoe as she followed their progress. Shortly after they turned for home, for the second and final time, they jumped the third last and one horse began to draw away from the others. His rider had a yellow jersey and a red cap. Glancing down at my racecard, I saw that the jockey was Alec Smith. Last Saturday's Hilton hero was on a roll. He'd had a treble at Plumpton on Monday, another at Lingfield on Tuesday and two more winners at Bangor-on-Dee yesterday. His mount was six lengths clear and showing no sign of stopping as he landed over the second last. He was even further in front as he neared the final fence, with Emma and I the only ones watching from the rails on the landing side.

We could hear him loudly counting down the strides as he came into the fence. He and his mount soared into the air and landed cleanly only for the horse to stumble. Smith sat like a limpet but to no avail. His mount struggled to regain his footing, stumbled a second time and Smith was ejected out of the side like a wartime pilot forced to abandon his plane. He landed heavily and lay still, seemingly winded, as the rest of the field galloped past. After several seconds, during which I wondered if I should duck under the rails and check whether he was alright, he got slowly to his feet. Taking off his gloves he strolled across and, grinning broadly, said: 'Great fucking game this. Just when you think you've cracked it, it lands you right back on your arse.'

After the ambulance arrived and collected him, Emma and I hurried to the winner's enclosure. I needed to speak to the successful trainer. There was no owner with Pete Allen and he gloomily informed me that the man was too busy trying to save his business, and had given his trainer instructions to sell all three of his horses. 'This one would be a good mount for an amateur,' he said hopefully. 'He's easy to handle, jumps well and he will get three miles.'

I might have been tempted had I not received Trevor Brownson's latest bill earlier in the week, together with a note that his fees were going up eight per cent in January. I shook my head. 'I'm sure you're right Pete but I can't afford to keep more than two in training.'

As I walked away from the subdued trainer – Allen could hardly have been more disheartened if he had trained Alec Smith's mount – and rejoined Emma, I was hailed by a shout. Arthur Jackson, tall, cheerful and sporting the fashionable but uncomfortable-looking haven't-shaved-for-four-days growth, came up grinning broadly and holding out his right hand. 'Hi Rod, how are you – and, more to the point, when will you be back riding again?'

Jackson was the on-course PR representative for Hedgers Bookmakers, one of the top six betting firms in the country. I introduced him to Emma and told him that, providing my doctor gave me the OK, I should be riding again in just over a fortnight.

'Great – and will Brown River be your first ride back?'

'Probably. Well, almost certainly.' I'd heard nothing from

Trevor about the horse's next race, and in truth the only alternative was Ezekiel. Unlike Alec Smith, owners were not exactly queuing up for my services.

'In that case you should be back with a winner. So unlucky at Sandown.' There were few who could turn on the charm like Arthur Jackson, even in bookmaking PR circles.

'Arthur, I'm writing something about *WeRthebestbets.com* What do you know about them?'

I sensed hesitancy. His expression and his manner changed from affable to wary. 'Are we talking on the record or off the record?'

'Either – or both.'

'OK, on the record, to start with anyway. They're new and making inroads fast. They're online only so they don't have the overheads of the rest of us. They know what they're doing but they're incredibly secretive. Nobody knows who they are, or even where they are.'

I scribbled into my notebook while he talked. I should have brought the tape recorder. He paused, seeing me struggling to keep up. 'You look them up on the internet. All you'll find are instructions how to register, how to place a bet and a lot of spiel about how good they are.

'They're attracting plenty of business and I won't deny that they are beginning to hurt us, and hurt everybody else too. But it's the secrecy I don't like. I find it suspicious and I fear that, sooner or later, they are going to be hit – so hard that they won't survive. A lot of punters will lose their money and the whole thing will give the bookmaking industry a bad name.'

He paused again, as I got to the end of the page, turned

over and kept writing. It was at times like these that I wished I'd learned shorthand. I'd once bought a book *Teach Yourself Shorthand* but I gave it up after the first page.

'And off the record?' I flipped over the remaining pages of my notebook to shut it, and I put my biro back in my pocket.

'Haven't I given you enough?' Arthur laughed. 'Off the record I'm convinced they are going to go bust. Maybe through over-extending themselves as a result of their obvious lack of experience. People think the bookies always win but sometimes they don't and we get taken to the cleaners. There are some very shrewd punters out there, you know. But what really concerns me – and this is definitely off the record, Rod. OK?'

I assured him I wouldn't use whatever he was going to tell me.

'I'm trusting you, Rod. What I think is going to happen is that they will deliberately go bust owing their punters a lot of money. They will pocket it and shut up shop, declaring bankruptcy. Their secrecy convinces me that their motives are criminal.'

'I see what you mean,' I said slowly, thinking about what he had said and realising that it made sense. Why the secrecy if it wasn't the plan to run off with their clients' money once they had expanded sufficiently to be handling a lot of it?

Arthur Jackson turned his attention, and his charm, to Emma. As I continued to ponder over the PR man's beliefs, he said he hadn't seen her racing before, was she enjoying it? He hoped he would see her again shortly. He touched an imaginary cap, said it had been lovely meeting her, and strode off towards the weighing room.

'What a nice man,' she said, adding with a smile and a glint in her eye: 'Good-looking too.'

I grinned, took her arm and steered her in the direction of the press room where she impressed the other two racing journalists by making them tea and coffee.

'Is there nothing to eat?' she asked, as she handed round the cups. Both men shook their heads. 'Not at this course, not under the new management,' said the *Racing Post* man.

'I'll see what I can do.' Ten minutes later she was back with a plate of sandwiches. 'Ask and ye shall receive,' she smilingly informed the scribes.

'Rod, you must bring this lady more often,' said the impressed Press Association representative.

Two races later I started on my report, leading with Alec Smith's quote, converting the four letter words to asterisks. I knew, almost no matter what happened in the last two races, that I wasn't going to get a better intro.

Nearing Andover I suggested we stop for an early supper, adding that I knew of a decent place on the Newbury side of the town.

'No Rod. We must get home.' I was surprised at Emma's response - and disappointed. I had expected that we would make an evening of it, and for the past hour and a half I'd been increasingly looking forward to it.

Thirty seconds passed before she turned towards me. 'That is, unless you don't think my cooking is worth eating.' I glanced at her. She was grinning broadly. I turned onto the A343 in a much more cheerful frame of mind.

Emma's cooking turned out to be a shepherd's pie that she had got up early to prepare. Handing me a bottle of cold beer, she took the pie out of the fridge, put it in the oven for 15 minutes before heating up frozen peas and beans. The result was mouth-watering, as were the stewed apples and cream that followed.

As we sat down next to each other on the sofa and she poured out coffee, I mentioned that one of the jockeys was holding a party on Saturday evening. Would she come?

There was a pause. 'Sorry Rod, I can't.'

I had a horrible feeling. 'Is it the same date as last Saturday?'

'Rod, I think it's time I levelled with you about Richard.' For the first time in my life I realised what people mean when they talk about their heart dropping to the pit of their stomach. 'Richard has asked me to marry him.'

I said nothing. Emma burst out laughing. 'Rodney Hutchinson, if there is one thing I've learned about you in the short time I've known you is that you are an open book. The expression on your face gives you away every time.' She laughed again. I couldn't see anything funny at all, quite the opposite. 'It's not serious. At least it is, but not in the way you think.'

She told me that she had been going out on an occasional basis with Richard Oakley for the past three years, at least when she was back in England between overseas stints. He was twelve years older than her and a partner in a firm of Oxford solicitors ('Unlike you, he likes the law'). Quite early on he had asked her to marry him – he had even taken a ring out of his pocket and gone down on one knee – but she had said no and had said the same when he had repeated the proposal on three subsequent occasions. 'My mother says I'm nuts. He's well off and a kind man. But I don't love him, and I'm not going to get married until I come across somebody I fall head over heels for.'

I relaxed sufficiently to ask why she kept going out with him. 'I dunno, maybe I shouldn't. But I don't want to hurt him by turning him away completely.'

'So he gets priority every Saturday evening?'

She laughed. 'Rod, there you go again. Listen, last Saturday I'd only met you a week and that was just in the surgery. That evening he asked me to go out with him this Saturday too. I hadn't even been out with you at that stage. How was I to know you would want to date me more than once?'

'And the next Saturday?'

'Next Saturday I'm going out with you. That's if you want me to.'

'I want you, Emma Johnson. And I want you now.' I moved in close, put my arms round her and pulled her into my chest. When I kissed her she responded with passion.

She was still doing so an hour and a half later when she pulled away, saying: 'Rod, it's time for you to go. I've got to get up in the morning - and so have you.'

I'd told her about my plans to return to Green Hill for further analysis of the training methods of Bob Arrows and Tom Swarter. As she pulled her jersey down over her bare breasts, I wished I hadn't.

It was raining, and depressingly dark, when the alarm on my

phone went off at 7.00am. What the hell was I doing getting up this early, and in weather like this, I thought as I turned over and went back to sleep.

Over a cup of coffee and a bowl of rice krispies two hours later reality looked rather different. I needed a good story - and the Green Hill gallops could well reveal one. The rain had cleared and the sun seemed to be breaking through.

By the time I got there, and climbed the hill, the second lot were just leaving. The Toyota Land Cruiser confirmed that the horses were Tom Swarter's, and they walked off two-by-two onto the lane leading towards their stables.

Had I missed Bob Arrows? There was no sign of more horses and, if Wednesday was anything to go by, his string worked first. After waiting for almost twenty minutes I was all set to go home, cursing myself for not having responded to the alarm, when a Land Rover appeared. It was pulling a trailer and it came to a halt in front of the wooden railings. Arrows got out and so did a passenger. The binoculars suggested he was a member of the stable staff. He looked little more than twenty, was wearing jeans, riding boots and a waterproof jacket and was carrying a helmet which he promptly put on, fastening the chin strap. The pair went to the back of the trailer and slowly pulled down the ramp. The stable lad went in and backed the horse out. It had saddle, reins and bridle already on. Arrows legged the lad into the saddle and handed him a whip. I noticed the lad was wearing rubber gloves, blue ones like my sister wears when she is putting her hands into hot water in the kitchen.

The horse was trotted round in a circle for a couple of minutes before going onto the gallop and breaking into a canter. He followed what I now realised was part of the established routine, once round the six furlong circuit at a rather sedate pace. But this time, instead of pulling up and circling before going again, the horse was immediately quickened into a racing gallop. When he branched off onto the straight section he was given a crack with the whip. The response was amazing. The animal found another gear and took off like a champion. Rather like Grey Somali on Wednesday, it took all his rider's strength to pull him up.

When he did, the horse was walked towards the trainer, still very much on his toes. While I couldn't say that his eyes were popping out of his head – I was too far away and my binoculars were not powerful enough – he was certainly far more jazzed up than I would have expected.

I watched as the lad got off, and led him round for ten minutes, before he and the trainer loaded the still over-excited horse into the trailer and drove away.

I waited a further ten minutes just in case they should come back. I didn't want them to spot someone coming down the hill carrying binoculars. When I neared the car I noticed that it's angle didn't look quite right. Maybe I'd parked on a sloping bit of ground. Then I saw the tyres. The two on the passenger side were flat. When I walked round to the driver's side the rear tyre looked fine but the front one had also got a puncture.

I'd carried a tyreweld repair outfit in the boot ever since car manufacturers had started economising by dispensing with a spare tyre, and just recently I'd bought a second one. If I was careful I should be able to get enough of the compressed air into the three punctured tyres to get me back to Reading.

I started with the passenger-side rear. But the weld, and

the air, seemed to be horribly slow to take effect. Then I spotted the cut in the sidewall. It was about two inches long and there was another just over a foot further round the tyre. I checked the other two flats and found, to my horror, that the sidewalls had been given the same treatment.

Then I saw the note. It was tucked under the windscreen wiper in one of those small resealable bags you use when putting meat into the freezer. I opened the bag and took out the note. No indentations so seemingly laser-printed from a computer. 'Next time it won't be just your tyres that get slashed.'

That shiver up my spine returned with a vengeance.

7

Neither Tom Swarter or Bob Arrows had runners at Newbury the following day, I was relieved to see. They had cost me the best part of £500 and taken four infuriating hours out of my day. The firm in Wantage luckily had the right tyres in stock but they were busy and the hour and a half they took to reach me seemed to drag for ever. Fortunately the two men brought a hydraulic jack with them and, while they weren't as slick as a Formula 1 team, they took barely ten minutes to replace the wrecked tyres. But I then had to drive to the depot to get the wheels aligned and pay the bill.

I'd told the attendant what had happened when I locked up in the press and officials' car park, and gave him a tip to make sure no-one tried it again. But I was still inwardly worried and, I hated to admit, more than a little scared.

The Major was doing the race-reporting but I was there to speak to a few people, in particular another of the bookmaker

PR men and Paddy O'Reilly, an Irish-born trainer who had finally become a success after twenty years struggling to survive on a handful of horses, and with only a few winners a season.

I ran him to ground in the spot reserved for the fourth horse after the opening maiden hurdle. His newcomer Tara's Conquest had run on strongly from quite some way back in a field of twenty.

'Ran well Paddy. Most encouraging for a first time.'

'Hi, how are you Rod?' I'd never spoken to him before but the fact that he knew me was a positive. 'Paddy,' I began. 'I'm writing an article about you and all your recent successes. Could I come and see you sometime to get some background information?'

'Sure,' he beamed. There was still a trace of an Irish accent even though I knew he'd been based in England for at least the last twenty years. 'When do you want to come?'

'What about Monday? Say I get to you after second lot? About 11.00am?'

'Couldn't be better. Do you know where I am?' He told me to make for Ogbourne Maisey and, as he gave me the directions from there, I wrote them down in my notebook.

Next on the list was Chris Thomas, PR for Betwins. I found him in the press room which was well patronised as it was a Saturday with several journalists filing copy for Sunday papers. Thomas, a small talkative man in his late thirties, cheerfully shook my hand, asked how the injury was progressing and when I would be back riding.

'Chris, I need a bit of assistance. Could we talk outside?'

He followed me through the door and round the side, out of the wind and out of sight of my competition. 'Chris, I'm writing an article about *weRthebestbets.com*,' I began as I took my tape recorder out of my coat pocket and held it a foot from his face. 'How do the big firms view them? Are they now serious competition?'

Thomas, far from being put out by what I feared he might regard as too probing a question, didn't hesitate. 'Not really. They are small, you see Rod. And they are online only. We have our own online section, as I'm sure you know, but the bulk of the betting is still in the shops in the High Street. That's a cash business and it's where most of the profits come from. Many punters still prefer it that way, I think for two reasons. One they know how much they can afford to spend and, two, because when they win they get a big kick out of being handed a pile of cash. If all you get is a note that the balance in your account has been increased by twenty quid, say, it's not the same thing at all.'

'Hm,' I thought about what he had said. 'But they seem to have grown rapidly. A year ago hardly anybody had heard of them. Now they are everywhere – adverts in the newspapers, on many of the internet sites. There are plenty of other online-only bookmakers but *weRthebestbets.com* is the one you hear about.'

'They're highly competitive, Rod,' answered Thomas. 'For example, they offer a point over the odds in the big races – something we, for one, couldn't afford to do –and that's a big attraction to punters.'

'Some people have told me they could go bust through inexperience.'

Thomas laughed. 'Of course, that's always a possibility.

Particularly with an outfit that's new and so small in comparison to a big, long-established firm like Betwins. Bookmaking is a difficult business. It's not just the punter who is gambling.

'Have they got the reserves to withstand big losses?' he continued. 'We all suffer them from time to time. And the fact that they are so new and unknown makes it a big question mark.'

I was glad I was using the tape recorder. It was going to be important to get these quotes right. 'I've heard complaints from some of the course bookmakers, Chris, that they are using unfair competition to get business. Like offering trainers over the odds and giving them their money back when big-name horses meet with a setback, in return for information about other horses in the yard.'

'I'm sure they do but – and I'd rather you didn't quote me on this – they are not exactly the only ones doing that. But I've never actually met anyone who has been in any sort of direct contact with them. I've tried, and so have other people in Betwins, to find out who is behind them and where they are based. But it's all hidden away through a series of Cayman Island companies. What I don't mind telling you, though Rod, is that this secrecy is suspicious. And it's hardly conducive to either confidence or belief in a bookmaking firm.'

He grinned and looked at the tape recorder. 'That do you?'

I thanked him and, still smiling, he walked off in the direction of the weighing room. I left after a further two races. The car park attendant gave me a cheerful thumbs-up as I approached. "Nobody messes with my cars,' he assured me.

The Regency Park Hotel, on the outskirts of Thatcham, was where Robbie Bolton was holding his thirtieth birthday party - or rather where Sheikh Mahmoud was paying for it, in appreciation of the champion jump jockey winning the Grand National for him in April.

The car parks were pretty full by the time I arrived shortly before 7.30pm – the email invitation had said '7.00pm, smart informal' which I took to mean a suit rather than a jersey. I was relieved to see several uniformed men directing vehicles into floodlit areas.

I had to wait at the desk while my name was checked with the guest-list before I was directed into a huge room swarming with half the British jump racing world, or so it seemed. One of the first people I spotted was Sarah Brownson. She saw me at the same time and waved me over to a large table occupied by her husband and a group of other people I didn't recognise, apart from her brother-in-law Jimmy. Sarah looked ravishing in a primrose dress and her dark hair swept up into what I presumed was called a beehive. I told her so as I gave her a kiss on the cheek.

Trevor stood up and came over to join us, holding a piece of paper in his right hand. 'Rod, I hoped you'd be here,' he began. "I've finalised plans for Ezekiel and Brown River. Ezekiel runs at Ludlow on Monday week, just a pipe-opener with Billy Black riding, and I've got you down for Brown River at Bangor-on-Dee at the end of that week. Will you be OK again by then?'

The four-week arm rest stipulated by Stuart would be just about up but I had to get race-riding fit in the meantime, and that meant riding horses at exercise. So much for doctor's orders. But, what the hell? I was fired with excitement at the prospect of race-riding once more. 'Definitely,' I replied. 'I'll make sure I'm fit too. I'm raring to go.'

'Good,' replied the trainer in a tone that suggested, to me at least, that he didn't really mean it. He looked round the table. 'You know Jimmy, I think.' The brother-in-law stood up and shook hands. 'My wife, Margaret,' he said, indicating a blonde woman with a rather lined face who smiled at me.

Trevor handed over the piece of paper and introduced me to the others. I shook hands with each, not really grasping their names for any longer than I grasped their hands. They passed in a blur as I savoured the prospect of returning to the racing saddle. I was about to move away when Sarah got to her feet and announced 'My favourite dancing partner is taking me onto the floor,' got hold of my hand and led me to the far end of the vast room where a band was playing and where several couples were already in action.

The music, alternating between slow and fast numbers, was at that moment given over to a particularly dreamy waltz and Sarah held me close. 'Now,' she said with a mischievous twinkle in her eye. 'Why haven't you told me about the beautiful blonde you took to Wincanton on Thursday? And why isn't she here tonight?'

I explained that Emma had an alternative engagement which she couldn't get out of. A slight embroidering of the facts but I didn't want to get into the whole Richard Oakley story. Indeed I'd been trying to shut it out of my own mind and, before Sarah had a chance to read my thoughts, I told her how I had met Emma and how we were going out tomorrow evening instead of tonight.

'I'm glad,' whispered my dancing partner as she held me even closer. We moved around in companionable silence and, to my mind at least, in almost sexual synchrony until the band switched rhythm and direction. 'Rod, I need to talk to you, somewhere where nobody can overhear us,' she whispered in my ear. 'You see the stairs over there?' She pointed to a staircase just visible behind the band. I nodded, wondering what was in her mind and hoping that it was the same as was in mine. 'Go up there now to the top floor and wait for me. I will be with you in five minutes, OK?'

I nodded. "Now, escort me back to the table and say goodbye loud enough for Trevor, Jimmy and Margaret to hear.'

I went up the stairs to a barely lit area with several rooms leading off it, and waited. Sarah's idea of five minutes seemed a long one but, just as I was wondering how much more time I should give her, she appeared smiling broadly. 'Sorry Rod. I got delayed.' She went to one of the nearest doors, opened it and turned on one of a panel of light switches. The room, with sloping walls and large windows set into them, seemed to have been converted from an attic. It was occupied by a large table with chairs all round it, and was clearly designed for meetings. Equally clearly, it was not going to be the sort of meeting that I'd been hoping for.

She sat down in one of the chairs and motioned for me to take the next one. She took hold of my hand and rested it on the table. Still holding it, she said: 'Now Rod, I want you to promise me to take great care for the next few weeks.

'Your articles are having a great impact, as I'm sure you know. You are being read by an ever-increasing number of people, and they take note of what you say. But Rod," my hand was squeezed. 'There are some ruthless people in racing and some of them don't like having the truth brought home to them.' I thought of Bob Arrows and Tom Swarter. And my tyres.

'Now, I'm not suggesting you tone it down a bit – I'm sure you won't and I wouldn't want you to – but just be careful not to leave yourself alone in dark, unguarded places. Like racecourse car parks. I know the press are often among the last to leave. Promise me.' My hand was squeezed again.

'Yes, of course Sarah. But what have you heard? Who's planning this attack, or whatever it is?'

She smiled. Still holding my hand, she shook her head. 'If I knew I would tell you. But what I can tell you is that it's more than just feminine intuition – and more than a premonition. Just something I heard. Not a lot but enough to make me frightened for you.'

She stood up, finally letting go of my hand. As I also got to my feet, she moved close and whispered 'Now kiss me.' The embrace was as passionate as could be, and my hand moved from the cheek of her bottom to her left breast before she broke away. 'One day, when this is all behind us, I want you to make love to me,' she said breathlessly. 'Now give me five minutes before you come down.'

As we went out of the door she switched off the light. At the same time a girl in a long white dress hurried past and shot down the stairs. As Sarah followed her at a more sedate pace, I reached in my trouser pocket for a handkerchief to wipe away the lipstick. I felt a rustle of paper. It was the note Trevor had given me.

It was typewritten and headed 'ENTRY/RUNNING PLANS' My name was on the next line and underlined. Then followed:

EZEKIEL: November 27 Ludlow   2 mile handicap chase W.Black (5)

BROWN RIVER: December 2 Bangor-on-Dee   2 ½ mile handicap chase Mr R. Hutchinson (7)

Billy Black claimed 5lb because he had ridden more than twenty winners but less than forty, while I claimed 7lb because I'd ridden less than twenty. Only three in fact, as Christopher Mayhew had pointed out in the Sandown stewards' room. Point-to-point winners didn't count.

I put the note back in my pocket as my mind returned to what Sarah had said. 'Just something I heard.' But what did she actually hear? And, every bit as important, who did she hear it from?

Twelve hours later I was in my tracksuit running beside the river towards its junction with the Thames, and then turning North West along Thames Path. For the past sixteen days I'd taken virtually no exercise – bar climbing Green Hill – and I had less than a fortnight to get race fit. I was only too aware that there was no substitute for riding a racehorse at a good pace but I didn't dare risk my barely-mended arm at this stage.

There were several other runners, particularly when I reached the Thames, some going slower than me and a few real athletes who effortlessly sprinted past and disappeared into the distance. As I ran I thought of Sarah – her warning rather than the sexual promise. I couldn't get its implications out of my mind. Or those of the note left on my windscreen.

I tried to switch these disturbing thoughts to my increasing physical effort as I stepped up the tempo. I was going to have to do this every day from now on, and really stretch myself each time if I was to be ready for Saturday week.

But my energy, or rather lack of it, soon began to take its toll and my worries switched to Emma and Richard Oakley. I found myself unable to stop thinking about what had happened between them on the previous evening. He obviously still held a considerable attraction for her, otherwise she would simply have dumped him. Maybe it was me she was thinking of dumping. By the time I was unable to run another stride I had more than half convinced myself that tonight's date was going to be our last. I sat down on one of the benches thoughtfully provided by the local council, and watched the grey water making its way towards London with the same inexorable inevitability as my thoughts making their way from depression to despair.

Five minutes of mental torture was all I could take before jogging slowly home. When I got back to the flat, I showered, made myself a cup of coffee and typed out the Chris Thomas tape-recording. After an early soup-and-sandwich lunch I did my questions for the Paddy O'Reilly interview. Both bits of work helped me forget about my rival for Emma's affections but the worries had returned with a vengeance well before I left at 6.00pm to pick her up. I was half-expecting her to ring to cancel but, when she opened her flat door resplendent in yellow blouse and pink waistcoat (with no buttons and open at the front), plus tight-fitting skirt to match, she confidently returned my peck on the cheek and gave every impression of being delighted to see me.

She chatted away happily on the fourteen-mile journey to Henley, making no mention of the previous evening. She seemed impressed when we drove into the car park of The

Angel On The Bridge, and more so when we entered the pub with its ceiling beams and open fire. I'd booked three days previously because it was a popular venue, particularly at the weekends.

After a drink at the bar we were escorted to our table which looked out onto the river, or rather as much as we could see of it from the lights on the outside of the pub. We sat side by side. After we ordered, with still no mention of the previous evening, I could wait no longer. 'How did things go with Richard,' I asked, trying to sound relaxed about it.

She grimaced. 'Not so good. He asked me to marry him - yet again.' She was watching my face closely, presumably for a reaction. Her laugh broke the tension. 'There you go again, Rod. Some people talk about wearing their heart on their sleeve. But I reckon you wear yours on your face.'

She gave me a dig in the ribs and laughed again. 'Actually, it wasn't funny – and I still feel guilty about the whole thing.'

I said nothing but raised my eyebrows in silent invitation for her to continue. 'I had to be blunt with him, more so than he deserved.' Her expression had turned serious, and there was no laughter as she continued: 'I explained that I was not going to get married until I fell in love and, while I liked him, I wasn't in love with him - and I now knew that I never would be. I said that it wasn't fair to either of us to go on seeing each other, and that this was the last time.'

'Did he accept that?'

'He didn't have much choice. But I still feel bad about letting him down like that, saying what I did.'

I took her hand. 'Emma, you didn't let him down. You were just being fair, letting him know where things stand.

And brave telling him to his face.'

She returned the handhold, squeezing mine tightly. 'Rod, you are so understanding.' She backed this up by kissing me on the cheek. Further debate was interrupted by the arrival of the waitress with the first course.

In the interval before the second I told her about my return to the saddle. She seemed to share my excitement, and I took Trevor Browne's piece of paper out of my pocket to show her the plans.

'W. Black?' She queried. 'Who's that?'

'He works in the yard. He's quite good.'

'Good enough to win the race?'

'Probably,' I hesitated and, sensing the couple at the next table taking an interest in the piece of paper Emma was still holding, I said quietly. "But the horse is not off.'

She looked puzzled. I put my head forward to whisper to her: 'He won't be trying. He's only going for a run to get him ready for the next time when I will be back riding him.'

Emma laughed. 'And I thought it wasn't meant to be fixed!'

'Shush.' I glanced to my right. They were now very obviously listening. 'Sometimes horses need an outing to get them ready,' I said rather louder, making sure they did hear.

'December 2? That's a Saturday isn't it? Pity, I'd have liked to be there.'

'Couldn't you get the day off? Work the Thursday instead?'

She shook her head. 'No. Saturday's the busiest day of the week. Maybe Ezekiel will run on a Thursday or a Sunday - when he is off.' She laughed. 'I'm picking up the jargon fast.'

An hour later we were in the car park and, after opening the passenger-side door for her, I walked slowly round the car looking at the tyres. Thankfully all four seemed fine.

'Is there a problem?' she asked as I got in and started the engine. I explained about my visit to Green Hill on the Friday and the ensuing trip to the tyre firm in Wantage.

'Goodness Rod. How awful. Who did it? And why?'

As we drove out of Henley I told her about watching the horses from the two different stables and my theories about what they might be doing.

'Do you think they know you're a reporter?'

'Looks like it,' I said quietly as I concentrated on overtaking a large lorry.

'Oh Rod, please be careful. It all sounds horribly dangerous.' She reached out with her right hand and rested it on my thigh, a gesture that blotted out the Arrows-Swarter goings-on and filled my mind with a mental picture of us both on her sofa.

I was sitting on it expectantly when she made the coffee in the small kitchen behind me. 'I didn't ask you about the party,' she said as she rattled cups and teaspoons. 'Who was the beautiful brunette in the primrose dress?'

I somehow concocted a laugh. I just hoped it sounded casual. 'Didn't your informant tell you it was my trainer's wife? Sarah Brownson?'

'Only that the two of you were dancing cheek-to-cheek.' I had a horrible thought that the source of her information might have been the girl in the long white dress who passed us at the top of the stairs. What else had she told Emma?

I laughed again. Even to me it appeared hollow and contrived. I smiled at her as she carefully placed two cups and saucers on the small table in front of us and sat down beside me. 'I will forgive you if you hold me cheek-to-cheek,' she whispered. The coffee was cold by the time the kissing and caressing came to a temporary halt.

An hour later, though, the break was rather more than temporary. She abruptly pushed away the hand that had wandered up the inside of her thigh, and sat up. 'Please Rod, no. This is too soon.' She shook her head, the blonde hair waving deliciously from side to side. 'I'm not the sort of girl that jumps into bed with every man she dates.'

'Sorry, I got carried away. It won't happen again.'

'Well,' she smiled and grasped the offending hand with both of her's. 'I hope it will, but not tonight. OK?'

I smiled back. This was one of the most beautiful women I'd ever met. I wasn't going to do anything that might put her off.

8

'Turn right in Ogbourne. Go for about a mile, the road bends sharply to the left and you'll see an iron gate between two stone pillars on your right.' Paddy O'Reilly's instructions were spot on. I reached out, pressed the intercom button and the gate opened. I parked in front of a small white house by the entrance to an L-shaped brick-built stable block.

'Morning Rod. Found the place OK?' The trainer, brown windcheater, jeans and riding boots, beamed as he shook hands, ushered me into the house and introduced me to a small grey-haired woman in glasses sitting at a desk with a pile of paperwork beside a computer - 'My wife Mary. She does everything. I'm just the link in the chain.'

Mrs O'Reilly, asking if I took milk and sugar in my coffee, disappeared into the kitchen while Paddy gestured me to one of the three armchairs facing the TV. He took the one next to me and, as I switched on the tape recorder and started going through my list of questions, the Irishman related his eventful life story.

Born in 1963 in Cashel, Co Tipperary, he was brought up in the village of Rosegreen just up the road from the world-famous Ballydoyle stables where his father worked for the great Vincent O'Brien. Paddy worked there for two years after leaving school with a totally inadequate leaving certificate. He made £500 when Thatching won at Royal Ascot – '6-1 but I was on ante-post at tens' he said, his tone suggesting this was an achievement in itself. But he lost every last penny when star two-year-old Storm Bird failed to live up to expectations two seasons later. 'Somebody broke in one night, hacked off his tail and he was never the same again.'

Glancing round the room as he talked, I was surprised to see so few racing photographs on the walls. There was just one of a horse and jockey (presumably him) jumping a fence at some course I didn't recognise, another of his and Mary's wedding and the third one of a small boy and girl holding hands.

Paddy hardly broke stride as he talked. I didn't know enough about Irish accents to pinpoint his but presumably it must have emanated from Tipperary. It had certainly been modified by his time in Australia. I listened, fascinated, as he explained how it had gradually dawned on him that he was not going to realise his dream of becoming a famous jockey if he stayed with the Flat racing stars at Ballydoyle, so he took the boat to England. There he got rides in National Hunt races but on bad jumpers – 'broke more bones than I rode winners' – before deciding to try his luck overseas. His accent, together with an embellished account of the role he played at Ballydoyle, proved a passport to jobs in top stables in Sydney, Cape Town and California. He returned to England at the age of thirty, met and married Mary, and set up as a trainer in Yorkshire. But it proved a precarious existence.

'I never had more than ten horses and most of them weren't much good. Money was always a problem. Sometimes I didn't have enough to pay the wages on a Friday so I had to bet during the week – and sometimes I lost it all.' He laughed.

Mary came in with the coffee on a tray, sat down in the remaining armchair and began to pour. 'Tell him about Gamblers Anonymous.'

Her husband chuckled. 'Mary insisted,' he recalled, smiling at the memory. 'I lost the wages two weeks in a row, and she said she was leaving me unless I stopped betting. She made me go to the meetings. Each person had to stand up and tell everybody how they became addicted to betting. When it was my turn, I told them about Thatching and said I had a hot tip for Saturday. The organiser took me to one side afterwards and told me not to come again. But, fek it, the horse won at 10-1. Most of the meeting were on. Some of them never went to the G.A. again!'

All three of us roared with laughter. 'But how come your luck changed?' I asked. 'I mean you had sixteen winners last season compared with two, three and only one in the previous three years. And you've had fifteen already this term.'

'Mr Mayhew,' answered Mary, sipping her coffee. 'We owe everything to Mr Mayhew.'

'Is that so?' I turned to Paddy.

'Yer man owns this place,' he answered. 'Had it not been for him, I'd probably have been forced to go back working as a stable lad until my OAP kicks in. God knows where we would have lived because we were broke.'

'Did he appoint you as his private trainer – or what?'

'Jaysus, no. I'll tell you what happened,' Paddy downed the rest of his coffee, put the cup and saucer back on the tray. 'I met him one day at the sales in Fairyhouse. He was in Ireland buying store horses at the big Derby Sale and I went there on the off-chance that I might pick up a few crumbs off the rich men's tables.

'He said he'd bought this place on the Wiltshire Downs. Used to be a decent jumping stable but it hadn't been used for a few seasons. He was doing it up. Would I like to come and have a look? Sure, says I. When I got here on the Monday, he said he had ten jumpers with various trainers but wanted them all under one roof. He was going to get a few friends to send some of their horses here too. There was this trainer's house which he was also doing up. Would I be interested?

'Is the Pope a Catholic, says I. We shook hands there and then - and I've never looked back. And at the age of sixty I'm finally living the dream.'

He got up, went to the table with the computer and picked up a large desk diary. 'When will you be cleared to start riding again?'

'Saturday week,' I replied, wondering what that had to do with anything.

'Hmm. Could you make the Friday?'

'At a push, yes. Why?'

'Mr Mayhew was here yesterday and I told him you were coming. He asked me if we could give you a ride or two, something with a decent chance. There is an amateur chase at Exeter on the Friday and Halton Manor would have a shout in that.'

'Great. Thank you very much.'

'I'd need you to come down and ride him first.'

'No problem. Just tell me when you want me.'

'Can you manage this Friday? He's doing a canter and then, if you could come again next Monday, we'll put him over a couple of fences.'

Stuart would have a fit. But what the hell? My arm felt fine and, if I strapped it up, I could be alright.

Paddy made a couple of notes in the desk diary and, returning it to the table, said: 'Come on, let's go and see your next winner.'

We walked up to the yard, the few grey wisps of hair Paddy still had left blowing in the wind like stems of wheat that the combine harvester had missed. I nodded to the half dozen or so lads going from box to box finishing off the morning's grooming. Paddy greeted each one by name and – after I'd switched the tape recorder back on - he reeled off a veritable Who's Who of each of the equine inmates, the races they had won and were going to win.

'This is Halton.' As if on cue, a chestnut with a broad white blaze stuck his head out of the second last box, still munching the hay he had pulled out of the net hanging from the wall on the inside of his stable. 'He's a bit slow but he stays longer than the mother-in-law and he loves the mud,' said his trainer as he fondled the horse's ears.

I gave Halton Manor a pat but, seemingly unimpressed, he promptly turned round and headed back to the haynet. As his trainer and I strolled towards my car, I was suddenly reminded of something. "Paddy. Do you know Tom Swarter and Bob Arrows?'

'The jigger twins?'

'The what twins?' I wasn't sure I'd heard right. Either that or I hadn't deciphered the accent correctly.

'You know what a jigger is?' Paddy broke off to speak to one of the lads about a horse in one of the end boxes. 'Did he eat up OK this time?'

When he rejoined me, I asked: 'You mean those things that get into your feet in hot countries if you don't have shoes on?' My only Kenya holiday had been marred by a painful session with a doctor using a sharp knife to dig out the unpleasant little insects, and their eggs, from the sole of my foot.

O'Reilly laughed. "Rod, I think you've led a sheltered life.'

'Why?' Maybe I had. Certainly I hadn't had to struggle to stay afloat like he had.

'Jiggers are electric whips. They use them in Australia, or they did when I was there. Could be they've tightened up since.'

I was not much the wiser. The trainer stopped in mid-stride and turned to face me. 'They're powered by a battery and, when the jockey presses a certain part of the whip, the tip delivers an electric shock to the horse. He gets such a fright that he bolts. A horse's natural reaction to anything that frightens him is to run like hell so the shock really makes him quicken.'

'But that is illegal under the rules, surely?' I was horrified. 'Everywhere. Not just Australia.'

'Course it is, and nobody uses them on the racetrack these days. What they do, though, is use them on the gallops at home. The rider shouts in the horse's ear just before he presses the button. Do this a couple of times and the horse associates the shout with the electric shock. All the jockey in the race has to do is shout a furlong out or so, and the horse will find another gear.'

'Bloody hell.' I thought back to Grey Somali at Sandown, and to the way the horses accelerated on the Green Hill gallop. Suddenly it all began to make sense.

'Cruel to the horses – some of them get turned into nervous wrecks,' Paddy acknowledged. 'But by God it works. If you're putting the money down you can have the bookies begging for mercy.'

'And it happens in this country?'

'I'm bloody sure it does. Word is that both Swarter and Arrows do it.'

I told him about what I'd seen from the top of Green Hill, about Brown River's race at Sandown and High Ransom at Haydock.

'That sounds like them. The two winners were well backed, I'm sure?'

'Yea. Almost off the board.'

'That's the jigger twins alright," Paddy smiled.' I've also heard they have a link with one of the bookies. They ask for a price for up to ten grand, say, and tell the bookmaker the horse is off. He gives them a point over the odds and promptly lays off the bet with other bookmakers plus a good bit more for himself.'

'Bloody hell. No wonder they slashed my tyres.' I told Paddy about what happened last Friday and the note under the windscreen.

'Rod, be careful.' He gripped the upper part of my right arm as his normal cheerful tone changed to one of concern. 'These two men are ruthless and what they're doing is criminal. If they ever got found out they could end up in prison, never mind losing their licences. If they think you're going to publish a story about them, they won't hesitate to silence you.'

I could almost feel the knife that destroyed my tyres being thrust into my stomach. 'OK Paddy. I understand. I'll think carefully about it all.' I just about managed a laugh. 'I certainly won't be jumping in with both feet.'

'And Rod. Don't mention my name in any of this, please. I've finally landed on my feet at long last. Mary would never forgive me if I threw it all away with my big mouth.'

I assured him I wouldn't. 'Good man.' He grinned as he clapped me on the shoulder. We continued on to the car where he shook hands and said: 'See you here Friday. We pull out shortly after eight.'

I said I would be in the yard in plenty of time. 'Great, look forward to it,' he smiled as he turned and headed back towards the house.

I drove slowly back through Ogbourne to the M4 thinking about what he had said. Was this also what Sarah had been warning me about?

Running up Thames Path in the slowly-clearing murk shortly after eight the following morning I went through yet again the problems that had been bothering me off and on for much of the previous day - and when I woke in the middle of the night.

I had two major, highly newsworthy articles but I couldn't fathom how to deal with them. Unlike the Paddy O'Reilly feature, which almost wrote itself and whose subject's colourful quotes virtually guaranteed a good read, the electric whip and *weRthebestbets.com* pieces were fraught with difficulty – and possibly danger.

'Sorry,' I swerved to avoid a middle-aged woman with two large hard-pulling dogs that I hadn't given enough space to, and splashed, as I found myself too late to sidestep a puddle. The electric whip needed exposing – I was still haunted by images of horses being terrified – but how to do it without overly drawing attention to the two trainers I now knew as the jigger twins? I wasn't worried so much about physical retaliation as the legal implications. Also I needed a comment from the BHA, and I had an uneasy suspicion that John Jameson already regarded me as a troublemaker repeatedly trying to dig up dirt.

I had more than enough comments about *weRthebestbets. com* from the big bookmaker opposition but nothing at all from the online upstart who was rattling their cages - if not their teeth as well. Nor did I have much likelihood of getting anything. Even more of a problem was that they were big advertisers with *sports-all.com* and Brett wasn't going to like it, whatever angle I adopted. But the subject couldn't simply be ignored.

It wasn't until the last mile of the homeward leg that I

found the solution, and it was beginning to rain. I put on a sprint to avoid getting completely soaked, and reached the flat just as the blackening clouds began unleashing their content in earnest. It was only after making myself a cup of coffee, though, that I picked up the phone.

The Major answered on the third ring. 'Rod, you OK?' His tone suggested he believed I wasn't. We might work for the same firm but it was rare for me to phone him.

I explained I had a problem, would appreciate his views and could I call to see him?

'Of course. I'm a bit tied up with previews and things this morning but I'll be finished by mid-afternoon, four o'clock anyway. Why don't you drop in then? You know where I am?'

'Only vaguely.' I knew he lived somewhere my side of Newbury but that was about all. I scribbled down the directions, said I'd be there at four, and went off for a much-needed shower.

Littleton proved well-named. There couldn't have been more than fifty houses. No pub, post office or even a shop. Just a road sign showing the name at each end of the village. The Hawthorns proved to be a large white house at the far end, with a thick hedge on each side of the gateless front entrance. A short tarmac drive divided the extensive lawn neatly in two and I parked by the front door.

The Major opened it before I'd had a chance to ring the bell. Even if you didn't already know he was ex-army, his clothes shouted it like a town crier. Cavalry twill trousers, suede shoes and a khaki-coloured jersey with leather patches on the elbows and shoulders, and his grey hair could not have been more immaculately brushed had he been about to go on parade.

'Hello Rod,' he greeted me cheerfully with an outstretched hand. 'Glad to see you found the place alright. Come in.' He led the way into a large sitting room. 'Take a pew. I'll be with you in a couple of minutes.'

I glanced at the two dralon-covered armchairs on each side of the fireplace and the matching sofa, but my attention was gripped by the large paintings and coloured photographs on the walls. One of the largest was of a group of horses jumping Becher's Brook, two of them were clearly about to fall while the leader was jumping it perfectly. There was also one of the Household Cavalry going past the Cenotaph.

On the other side of the room was a head and shoulders oil painting of an attractive woman in her thirties, and a few yards to her left was another large and striking coloured photo of a horse clearing a fearsome-looking timber-barred obstacle and jumping straight into a small lake. There was water splashing up in all directions and the horse's rider was standing in the irons letting out a long length of rein to give the horse his head.

'Hi, I'm Heather.' I turned, startled. I hadn't heard her come in but I immediately knew that this was The Major's daughter. Dark-haired and good-looking, she was in her early twenties wearing navy jeans and a polo-neck jersey to match. She was sitting on a four-wheeled scooter equipped with a steering wheel.

'You looking at the family album?' She smiled as she steered the scooter towards the oil painting. 'That's Mummy.' She then silently made for the two photographs that had first caught my attention. 'That's Daddy in the lead but he fell at the next. He never had much luck in the National. I think he only got round once in five rides.'

'And this one? Is that the Cenotaph.'

'Quite right.' She seemed both surprised and impressed. 'He's the one on the horse in front.'

'And the one of you over there?' I pointed to the three-day event photograph. 'Is that Badminton?'

'Yup. On Ditchling. We were third that year. Might well have won had he put in a clear round in the showjumping. Such a brave horse in the cross country. Terrible tragedy that he was killed 12 months later.'

'Oh. What happened?' I realised, almost as the words came out of my mouth, that I shouldn't have spoken.

Her manner changed from cheerful to almost sadness as she slowly related: 'He slipped on take-off at the fence after that one.' She pointed to the water-splash picture. 'I was thrown over the fence, he turned a somersault and came down on top of me. He broke his back and had to be put down. I sometimes feel I would have been better off if I'd been put down too.'

I didn't know what to say. An uncomfortable few seconds of eerie silence was broken by The Major's return. 'I see you've met Heather,' he said cheerily. 'Come and sit down.'

'You two chat,' said his daughter as she steered towards the door. 'I'll go and organise the tea.'

'Now Rod, tell me what's on your mind.' The Major sat down in the chair to the right of the fireplace and I took the one on the other side.

'Two things, really Charles,' I began. I pointed out that I had plenty of comments from the bookmaker opposition but none at all from *weRthebestbets.com* and nor could I find them; even their advertising with *sports-all.com* was done through an agency which said it was under strict instructions not to release any contact details. And also I couldn't afford to write anything that was going to upset Brett.

'Did you speak to him?' The Major broke in.

'Brett? No. Not yet anyway. But Charles, I feel that I must get everything sorted, write the article and then show it to him. If I start going to him with questions along the way, he's going to say no there and then.'

The Major chuckled. 'I can see him doing just that. The last thing he wants is to upset an advertiser, particularly a big one like *weRthebestbets.com*.'

'But Charles. That's the point in a way – or one of them anyway. They're the new kid on the block and they're making a huge impact. People want to know about them.'

A buzzer sounded, seemingly from somewhere behind his head. 'Sounds like the tea,' he said, getting to his feet. 'Back in a minute.'

It was more like three before he reappeared pushing a trolley with his scooter-mounted daughter just behind him. The sitting room door, presumably with the aid of some sort of spring, slowly shut behind her.

'I'll be mother,' her father said smilingly as he sat down and pulled the trolley towards him. 'Milk and sugar, Rod?'

Heather collected the tea cup and, holding a plate of biscuits in her other hand, somehow switched the scooter into motion and steered it towards me. I thanked her and, putting both items on the small table beside my chair, I remarked how well she seemed to manage everything.

'Thanks Rod.' She seemed pleased about what she clearly regarded as a compliment. 'It's amazing what's available for people like me. You should see my car. I just press a button, the whole of the back lifts up, I drive the scooter in, press another button and I'm in the driving seat.'

'Heather's very good,' added her clearly proud father. 'She also teaches riding for the disabled several times a week.'

'And I'm going to do a whole lot more than that,' said Heather, by now back to what I later found was her normal cheerful and determined manner. 'My aim is to teach people three-day eventing. I may not be able to ride anymore but I know how to do it, and do it well.'

'She certainly does,' said her father as he sipped his tea. 'Anyway, Rod, carry on. You were saying? *weRthebestbets. com*?'

I briefly recapped. My difficulty was that the other bookmakers were also big advertisers. I had to explain about the new opposition, the problems the online operator posed and it's benefit to the punter.

The Major silently rubbed his chin with the palm of his right hand, seemingly deep in concentration. 'I think you have it, really,' he said slowly, after a pause lasting a good twenty seconds. 'The benefit to the punter. I think that should be your theme.

'This is something relatively new, it's growing fast, both in terms of turnover and popularity. The big bookies don't like it because they can't compete. No overheads with online, while the established names have betting shops plus on-course presence - or contacts at the very least. Obviously you can't publish what their people are saying about *weRthebestbets. com* deliberately planning to go bust owing a lot of money. That doesn't hold water anyway. Certainly not to me. I can't believe anybody in their right mind is going to go to all the trouble of building up a business and reputation just to defraud people. And anyway why should they want to? They are clearly making good money. Why throw away the ATM when it's churning out cash for you?'

'And Brett? Do you think he will be alright with that approach?'

'Why wouldn't he be? In fact, I would have thought he would be delighted. You are going to please *weRthebestbets. com* with positive publicity – and the big boys will welcome their printable views being quoted.'

'Sorry to interrupt.' Heather turned her scooter to face the door and said: 'Daddy, I'll be upstairs for the next hour or so. Rod,' she turned her head towards me. 'Lovely to have met you. See you again soon, I hope.'

I watched, fascinated, as the door opened as she neared it and then closed again after the scooter had gone through it. 'Will it go upstairs as well?'

Charles laughingly shook his head. 'We had a lift installed once we found out how she was going to have to live life after her accident.'

'She seems to cope remarkably well.'

'She does,' he said slowly before looking in the direction of the painting on the far wall. 'But losing her mother was a bitter blow to both of us.'

I was uncomfortably aware that I didn't know what to

say next. Should I return to my problems – somehow they seemed so minor that I shouldn't even be here discussing them. Or was I expected to ask why Mrs Cavendish died.

'What happened?' The long pause after my question convinced me I'd gone for the wrong option.

'Lung cancer.' Charles said eventually, with a pained expression on his face. 'She'd given up cigarettes more than ten years before but seemingly the damage had already been done. She was on chemotherapy but it nearly killed her, and after six months she was dead.'

'Charles, I'm so sorry.'

He shook his head and, after what seemed like an age, he smiled. 'Anyway you said you had two problems. What's the second one?'

I wasn't sure it was even worth mentioning. Compared with the difficulties he was facing, the electric whip issue was about as significant as the dregs left in my tea cup. But, I reminded myself, this was one of the two things I'd asked to speak to him about. And the cruelty to the poor horses involved meant it had to be exposed.

I explained how the Sandown race and Oliver Chester-Beatty's comments had aroused my suspicions, how these intensified when I witnessed High Ransom in the Haydock winner's enclosure and saw what was happening on the Green Hill gallop. But I was careful not to mention Paddy O'Reilly and what he had told me.

'Hmm.' Charles rubbed his chin a second time. 'Have you got enough to go on, I wonder? Apart from any other consideration there is the libel aspect. As a former solicitor, I'm sure you know that in a libel case it is not enough to say that what you wrote was true. You have to be able prove it. In other words, the writer is guilty unless he can prove otherwise.

'Also, if these two trainers are doing what you believe they are, they are quite likely to try and silence you in one way or another. Have you considered that?'

I told him about the damage done to my tyres, and the note under the windscreen.

'Christ!' He was shocked. 'Rod, for God's sake lay off.' He sat up in his chair and, leaning forward, asked: 'Why are you chasing this story? There are a hundred other things you could be writing about. Is it because you are trying to get revenge for losing the race at Sandown? If you are, you shouldn't be a journalist at all.'

I was surprised at the intensity of his concern. 'No Charles, nothing like that. I know not to use my columns to fight my own battles. But I am concerned about the mental damage they are inflicting on horses – and what they are doing is not only against the rules but criminal. It's also unfair on everyone else who plays the game straight.' I managed a grin. 'Or, should I say, reasonably straight.'

'But the dangers, Rod? Surely, you see that the note was intended as a warning? Keep your nose out or you'll get knifed.'

'But Charles. If we all adopted that point of view, evil would prevail over good in everything.'

Charles slowly shook his head. 'No, Rod. You seem to think that, as a racing journalist, you should fight racing's battles. The BHA employs an army of investigators, officials and others to do that. By all means tip them off. But don't try to do their work for them. If you carry on like that you will be in mortal danger,' he paused before adding quietly: 'The sort of mortal danger I faced in the Falls Road in two tours of Northern Ireland at the height of the Troubles - when half the population wanted us dead.'

'OK. Point taken.' This time it was me talking quietly and slowly. 'I'll think again.'

Charles seemed to lighten up, but only a little. 'Have a drink, and we can both relax.' He got to his feet and went to the far corner of the room where I could see a trolley with various bottles on it. 'Whisky?'

'Just a small one, Charles – and plenty of water. I've got to drive.'

He handed me a crystal glass, three-quarters full. 'Cheers.'

I sipped. But I could feel the tension between us. It was like a rope pulled so taut that the slightest extra pressure would snap it.

Five minutes of strained small talk later I downed the rest of my glass and got to my feet. 'Thanks for all the advice Charles. I much appreciate it.' Making a determined effort to smile, I added: 'I'll do what you say and lay off the subject.'

'Thank God for that.' He laughed before ushering me through the door into the hall. A framed photograph on the wall caught my attention. It was of Boris Johnson presenting a trophy to Charles who said: 'I think I'm right in saying it was the first time the Horserace Writers' Association succeeded in getting a sitting Prime Minister to make the presentations at the naps lunch.'

'You won it, I presume?'

'Yea.' He paused. 'Won't this time, though. My tips are starting at too short a price, and I'm not sure why.'

He accompanied me to the car. As I got in, I wound down the window to thank him again. He gave a wave in acknowledgement before bending down to put his head level with mine. 'Take it easy, Rod. I don't want to be writing your obituary after you've been found in a ditch with your throat cut.'

His words stayed with me all the way back to Reading. Much as I tried, I found I couldn't think about anything else.

9

Later, when I looked back over the next three days, I realised that I was increasingly preoccupied, not by the articles I was writing or by the mental debate about whether I should write them, but by my imminent return to race-riding.

The nearer that came the more excited I got. I'd known from as far back as those early point-to-point reports that it was riding in the actual races that fired my enthusiasm for the sport - not writing about other people riding and training, fascinating though that was. More than anything I wanted to be a success in the saddle. Maybe one day become champion amateur and, of course, ride in the Grand National.

Not even Emma meant that much, even though she was fast assuming a deeper place in my affections than any girl I'd ever dated - including those teenage romances when I seemed to fall in love every time. We had a date to remember on the Thursday when I joined her in taking a day off, going to London, walking in Hyde Park, feeding the ducks in the Serpentine and having lunch at a little café nearby. In her flat that evening it was me who brought our passionate caresses to an end by pointing out that I had to be up early the following morning.

I had already written and put on the website the Paddy O'Reilly article followed by the *weRthebestbets.com* feature which attracted a lot of comments, even though several of the writers seemed to have trouble spelling the name correctly. As I'd pointed out in the article, it may be cumbersome but it powerfully conveyed its own advertising slogan. As The Major had predicted, the piece went down well with Brett.

I still thought about the electric whip issue, though, and I remained more than half-convinced that I should tackle it. But the other half told me I didn't have the time this week, and the subject-matter would still be there waiting for me if I felt the same way next week.

The one cloud on the horizon was my arm. When I first went to see him, Stuart had spoken of being alright to resume 'in four weeks.' Even three weeks was not until next Monday and Stuart had been very specific about 'no riding in the meantime.' He had repeated the warning on the follow-up visit, explaining that any pressure could cause the crack to spread.

I had a tendency to worry and I found it difficult not to let problems give me sleepless nights. And the nearer I got to Friday the more anxious I became. Sometimes I was able to overcome what I regarded as a flaw in my character by asking myself what would be the worst thing that could happen if the worries turned into reality. But in this case I had a pretty good idea, and it was alarming. The arm would have to be rested, and encased in plaster, until it healed completely. That would take at least two months, with probably a further month out of plaster, before I could ride again. Yet another month before I would be race-fit, and that would take me to the end of March. By that time rides for Paddy O'Reilly and Christopher Mayhew would be gone beyond recall.

Riding a horse at a gallop, particularly if he pulled as hard as many did, would test the crack to its limits and an even earlier problem was getting on the animal in the first place. Racehorses do not stand still - like their less highly-strung counterparts in a riding school - while the pilot puts his foot in the stirrup iron and hauls himself into the saddle. And nor, usually, is there anybody to hold the animal while you mount. You have to lead him out of his box - already saddled and bridled – and, putting one hand on the pommel of the saddle and the other on the rear part of it, you vault onto the horse's back, slip your feet into the stirrups and grab the reins before his walk accelerates into a trot. Or faster. The pressure exerted on your arms in this manoeuvre is considerable.

I was still thinking about how to get through this when the metal gate opened in response to the intercom button at 7.45am on Friday. I again parked in front of the trainer's house, and this time I took my whip and helmet out of the boot before making my way up to the flurry of activity in the stable area. The staff were going in and out of the boxes carrying saddles and bridles while the trainer, wearing the same windcheater, jeans and riding boots as on Monday but this time plus a flat cap, gave orders and instructions.

'Morning Rod,' he smilingly greeted me. 'Ready for action?'

'I sure am.' I wasn't going to admit about the worrying.

'Brenda,' he called out to a teenage girl in brown jodphurs, bright yellow jersey and a helmet covered by a red 'silk.' Rod here is riding Halton. Give him a hand, will you?'

I followed her into the tack room, was given a bridle and saddle, and listened as she gave me a running commentary on the horse, his likes and dislikes, while we walked towards the end of the line of boxes. The white blaze had his head out, taking a keen interest in all the goings-on. Brenda went into the box, put the bridle over his head, checked that the bit was comfortable in his mouth and removed the head-collar in about thirty seconds while I had got no further than putting the saddle on his back.

'He blows out a bit so you'll need to tighten the girths when we're circling,' she said as she led him out into the yard. Clearly there was no risk of Halton Manor trying to take off as I struggled to get aboard. Seemingly, too, I needn't have worried about vaulting into the saddle. As she halted the horse outside the stable, Brenda reached down to grab my booted calf with her right hand and powerfully lifted it upwards. I was sitting down in the saddle before I had a chance to even think about my arm. It hadn't experienced any pressure whatsoever.

Gratefully heading towards the horses that were already circling, the excitement flooded through me, drowning my fears like a dam bursting its banks. Halton Manor added to my delight by taking his place in the string like an old soldier lining up on parade. I knew immediately that he wouldn't try and take off even when we got onto the gallops. My arm, and Stuart's handiwork, would live to face another day.

We circled for five minutes, while other horses were led out of their boxes and mounted, before going through a gate at the back of the yard and up a seemingly well-worn path to the higher ground.

'What are we going to do?' I asked Brenda, riding alongside me on an excitable liver chestnut with three white socks and a ragged blaze down the front of his face.

'Going up to High Down,' she answered. 'Stop it. you bugger - just bloody behave.' Her mount responded by throwing his head around as he noisily played with the steel bit in his mouth. 'We'll canter four furlongs and come back at half speed.'

She spoke about the various horses in the string for the next fifteen minutes until we reached a five-barred wooden gate, incongruously placed without anything anywhere near it. The horses, fourteen of them, circled round the gate. Many of them were by now jigging excitedly on their toes. They knew what was coming. Their riders paired up and set off, Noah's Ark style, but with about twenty yards between each of the seven couples. Brenda's mount and Halton Manor were the last two to leave and we travelled on a long stretch of level springy turf, not at a canter but at a steady gallop. My horse travelled easily within himself and seemed relaxed, certainly in contrast to Brenda's mount who clearly wanted to go a lot faster and battled with her to let him do so.

She had a lot more difficulty in pulling up than I did. 'Bloody sod. Never listens,' she said breathlessly as we resumed circling, but this time in pairs. Looking round at the surroundings, I could see the village well below us. We were quite high up and there was a strong wind blowing by this stage but, fortunately, no sign of the rain that I knew was forecast.

'You OK Rod? We're going back now.' Brenda began to turn her mount who whipped round excitedly, and took off with his rider swearing as she struggled to restrain him. Halton Manor, in contrast, continued to behave like a perfect gentleman, settling easily alongside as we travelled into the wind at a two-mile racing pace. Half-speed, I had long since learned, was as much of an understatement in the racing world as the word canter.

We led the rest of the string until pulling up near a maroon Discovery beside which was a binocular-using Paddy O'Reilly. My lack of fitness was all too evident – to myself, although I hoped, not to Paddy. I was decidedly short of breath. Again we circled while the trainer spoke to each of us in turn. 'Any better today, Brenda?' I heard him ask. 'Nah, boss. Pulled like buggery all the way there and most of the way back.' She was still struggling for air. 'Maybe we should let him work on his own next time.'

O'Reilly didn't answer but, turning towards me, said: "How was it Rod? Arm OK?'

'Perfect. I'd forgotten all about it.' True, I had once I was in the saddle– and I'd been excited and thrilled by the ride, particularly on the return trip when we'd gone so much faster. 'Horse feels great too.'

Again the trainer didn't answer, just moved on to the two riders behind us. After a few minutes Brenda led us back down to the path towards the stables, but this time we went in single file and for the first time in almost an hour her horse relaxed.

Back in the yard I led my mount into his box and returned his saddle and bridle to the tack room before going off to thank Paddy for the ride, and confirm arrangements for Monday's schooling session. "Mary's waiting for you in the house," he said before I had a chance to say anything. 'I'll be there in ten minutes.'

Much to my surprise, and delight, Mrs O'Reilly – this time with an apron on – plonked a plate of bacon, egg and fried bread onto the kitchen table and bid me sit down. 'Tea alright?' she asked, placing a cup in front of me and pointing to the large teapot at the other end of the table.

'That was a lovely article on Paddy,' she said. 'Mr Mayhew thought it was good too. He was talking to Paddy about it when he rang last night. Such a nice man, always so helpful.' She was in such a chatty mood that I only had to nod now and again as I tucked into my breakfast.

I'd finished by the time her husband came in, took off his cap and windcheater and sat down while his wife broke another egg into the frying pan. 'Rod, I forgot to say thank you for the article. Very good – and much appreciated.'

'I was telling him about what Mr Mayhew said about it,' said Mary as she deftly flipped the egg onto a piece of fried bread and put the plate in front of her husband.

'For sure. Plenty of people mentioned it to me at Taunton yesterday – and Rod'......he paused as he chewed on the first mouthful..... 'might have a bit of news for you.' He transferred another piece from his plate to his mouth. 'I was talking to Johnny Evans in the trainers' tea room. You know him?'

'Vaguely.' I had a mental picture of a small man who trained in a small way but had a lot to say for himself.

'Trains Gloucester way. Said he knew who owns that

betting website you wrote about. 'Bet you don't, says I.'

"Buy me a bit of that there cake to go with my tea and I'll let you into the secret," he said. So I did cos I tought you'd like to know.' I'd noticed that Paddy had a tendency to drop his aitches, Irish-style, when he got excited.

'And who is it, says I.' He looked at me as expectantly as he must have looked at Johnny Evans. 'Guess.'

I shook my head and smiled. 'Tell me. The suspense is killing.'

'George Rickards?'

'Who?' The name meant nothing to me, and I said so.

'George Rickards. And guess who trains for him?'

I shook my head again, this time glancing at Mary who, judging by her broad grin, already knew what was coming.

'Tom Swarter and Bob Arrows. Got about ten horses with each of 'em.'

'Bloody hell.' The significance hit me like a thunderbolt. The jigger twins, their electric whips, the money pouring on Grey Somali and High Ransom, the horses' over-excited state in the winner's enclosure, the undetectable fear-induced adrenaline – it all fell into place like the final pieces of a jigsaw.

'Now be very careful, Rod.' Paddy could see my mind working. 'These two men are dangerous. And ruthless.'

Saturday I went to Ascot, not to do the report – The Major regarded that as his right even though winter jumps meetings there bore as little resemblance to the June fashion spectacular as a blackbird does to a peacock – but to talk to people, two in particular.

It hadn't taken me long to decide that the electric whip issue was going to be my next big article. Charles's advice might have been sensible but he was an old-timer stuck in his ways and I certainly wasn't going to be put off by a few threats. I wouldn't be much of a journalist if I did. In any case I faced bigger dangers every time I rode in a race, in particular falling and being treated like a human football, kicked around in a sea of lethal aluminium-tipped hooves, each blow delivered with the power of half a ton behind it. If I could treat that sort of thing with equanimity, a nick with a knife hardly seemed worth bothering about. At least that's what I kept telling myself.

I'd spent much of Friday researching. I was surprised – astonished might be a better word – at how much the subject had hit the headlines in the past. They'd had electric whips in races in Singapore, and in South Africa cattle prodders (used as a 'training aid') had proved such a threat that the rules made it an offence for a trainer to even keep one on his premises. My task was made easier, and my article more newsworthy, by a small piece in that day's *Racing Post*, mentioning the case of an Australian trainer who had been banned after being found to have four jiggers in his bedroom. The report finished by posing the question of whether such instruments could be being used by UK trainers.

It gave me the lead I needed for my questions, and this time I intended to go higher than John Jameson. Hopefully the two men I sought on the drizzle-dampening grey afternoon would regard my questions as relevant and not those of a sensation-seeking journalist.

Target number one was Eugene Edwards, the newly appointed chief veterinary officer. I'd spoken to his predecessor on several occasions but the new man I only knew by sight. I tackled him as he exited the parade ring when the opening-race runners were being led out prior to cantering down to the start.

I didn't get far. 'I don't discuss anything like that,' the hatless, brown-overcoated figure replied, his tone and expression as unfriendly as if I had accused him of beating his wife. Hardly breaking stride, he brushed past me and grim-facedly continued towards the weighing room.

I'd half-expected something like this. Officialdom on the racecourse tended to be friendly but being quoted on controversial issues was a no-no with many of them. Apart from any other consideration, they feared their superiors wouldn't like it.

Target number two was the ultimate superior. I was pretty sure William Sommerville, chairman of the BHA, would be at the racecourse. But where? I went to the door of the main lunch area and spent a couple of minutes searching the packed room. One of the first people I recognised was Sarah Brownson. She was sitting with Trevor, brother-in-law Jimmy and his wife Margaret. I smiled and waved as she looked up and saw me. She didn't respond. Instead she looked away and concentrated on her conversation with Margaret.

I was surprised, and not a little disappointed. But, reminding myself of why I was there, I continued to search. But no sign of the main man. I went up to the top floor of the grandstand to the directors' dining room but the official on the door would allow me no further.

'Mr Sommerville, you said? Just a minute.' He stuck his head round the door but in such a way that I couldn't see in. 'He's here but I can't let you go in. More than my job's worth.'

I said I would come back later. The third race was sponsored so I thought he would be likely to go into the parade ring beforehand to meet the representatives of the firm that was putting up the money.

Sure enough Sommerville, a man in his early fifties wearing a smart fawn coat and no hat despite the drizzle, was there being introduced to a succession of people with his cheerful charm raising smiles at every turn. I'd met him a few times and been impressed by his friendly manner. He treated me as an equal with an interesting job to do, unlike many in racing's authority who looked on journalists with undisguised suspicion.

As the horses were going out of the ring, and the human element leaving it in the opposite direction, I made for Sommerville.

'Hello Rod,' he greeted me with an outstretched hand and a grin. 'How's the news hound?'

'William, there was a piece in the *Racing Post* yesterday about an Australian trainer who hid electric whips in his house...'

Before I could say anything else Sommerville burst out laughing. 'Yes, I saw that. Had four of them in his bedroom. I would have thought one would have been enough.' He laughed even louder. 'Sorry, couldn't resist that.'

I smiled briefly. 'The article also spoke about whether these sort of whips could be being used by trainers in this country.'

'What have you heard?' Sommerville's jocular tone turned serious.

'Well, nothing definite. But I've seen a few things that made me wonder, particularly after reading that article.'

'Such as?' We were now the only ones still in the parade ring. Everybody else had disappeared in the direction of the stands.

'Horses in a very excited and distressed state in the winner's enclosure - with their eyes popping out of their heads. And after being heavily backed.'

'That could mean any number of things, Rod - as you well know. And it would be well-nigh impossible to use an electric whip on the racecourse. Any jockey doing that would be found out immediately and banned for a very long time.'

Sommerville paused, looking me straight in the eye. 'But, and you can quote me on this, we regard using anything like an electric whip on a horse at home, or on the training grounds, as horrific animal cruelty. And we would certainly make an example of any trainer found doing that.

'As of today we have no suspicions about such things being used in this country. But it is something we are watching out for, particularly after what has been happening in Australia. OK?'

'Yes. Thank you William.' He nodded, smiled and hurried through the now-intensifying rain in the direction of the stands.

'Rod.' I turned, surprised, to find Trevor coming up behind me. 'Ezekiel goes in the second at Ludlow on Monday.

Confirmed the declaration this morning. Will you be there?'

'Possibly. Probably. Just have to check with my boss where he wants me to go. How's the horse?'

'He's doing OK. He'll need the run and two miles is too short. But the race should bring him on for when you're back.' Trevor, giving me no time to answer, patted my shoulder and quickened his step as he also made for the stands.

I went to the press room instead and, blanking out the commentary and the comments of the other journalists, grabbed an empty chair and scribbled down as much of William Sommerville's comments as I could remember.

'Got a good story?' Charles was standing behind me, smilingly looking down at my notepad.

'Not really. Just writing down a few things before I forget them.' I tried to cover the notebook with my racecard in a way that didn't suggest I was intent on hiding anything. But I breathed a silent sigh of relief when Charles joined the exodus making for the winner's enclosure.

I decided to get out before he returned and, packing everything into my laptop carrying-case, I headed for the reserved car park. I was ten yards from the BMW when I saw the note tucked under the windscreen. I turned and headed back towards the car park attendant who I'd just passed. 'Joe.' He was one of the few attendants I knew by name. 'Did you see who put that note on my windscreen?

The white-coated figure, well into his sixties, turned and came towards me, a worried expression on his face. 'No, Mr 'Utchinson. Nobody went near your car.' He looked closely at the note which had been protected from the rain by being enclosed in a small plastic bag, ominously like the one in the

Green Hill layby. I lifted the windscreen wiper, picked up the bag and got into the car.

I drove off wondering what the note said and who had put it there. Neither Bob Arrows or Tom Swarter had a runner - I'd checked that before I left home. But I was damned if I was going to give whoever wrote it the satisfaction of watching me reading it.

All the way through Bracknell, onto the motorway and into Reading I mentally ran through the articles I'd written recently to think of anyone I could have annoyed sufficiently for them to threaten me. The jigger twins, and the *weRthebestbets.com* boss they trained for, were the most obvious candidates.

Not until I reached the flat, by which time I'd got myself into such a state that I had been increasingly - and dangerously - unaware of the other traffic, did I reach for the little plastic packet. My garage door – there were four others and mine was the second from the end -responded to the remote as I did so. I didn't drive in but turned off the engine and unsealed the bag. I was as nervously expectant as a mother on her way to the maternity hospital, and I had to get a grip to stop my hands shaking.

I extracted a small piece of white paper folded in half and, as I did so, I smiled and relaxed. The rounded letters could only have come from a woman and I immediately realised it was from a special one.

'Hi Rod,' it began. 'Sorry I couldn't talk. Hope to see you soon. All my love, Sarah.' On the next line were four small crosses followed by 'PS. Please remember what I said. My information suggests that next week could be particularly dangerous.'

I read it through twice more, still smiling. But back inside the flat I wondered about the PS. What did she mean? Who did her 'information' come from? And what exactly was it that her informer was implying could happen next week?

10

I packed the car early and carefully on Monday. I had a long day, a tight schedule and there would be no time to come back if I'd forgotten anything. At 6.00am it was bitterly cold, the frost still on the ground even in the town, but thankfully the forecast was for a mostly dry day with rain not expected until evening, if at all.

It didn't really get light until I turned off the M4, and from thereon there was almost no traffic. I reached the stables just before 8.00am, and I could see Paddy standing in the middle of the yard when I parked the car. He turned and strolled towards me as I walked briskly, helmet in one hand and whip in the other, to do my bit in getting Halton Manor saddled and bridled.

'Morning Rod,' he grinned, no cap on this occasion but the windcheater looked thicker than the previous time. Looking closely, I realised he had an extra jersey on underneath. He was also wearing gloves.

'Fecking freezing,' he said, banging his hands together and breaking into a broad grin. 'See you were careful not to mention the jigger twins in your article yesterday.' He was referring to the electric whips piece that I'd filed under the headline *'BHA boss warns of horrific animal cruelty - action to be taken.'*

I'd quoted William Sommerville in full, and explained what had happened around the world with particular reference to incidents in Australia. I'd added: 'The racecourse rumour mill has been busy with suggestions that one or two unscrupulous trainers have been using these so-called jiggers, and have made arrangements with certain bookmakers to get their money on at good prices in return for information that "the horses can't lose."'

By racing standards it was sensational stuff and Emma, who had spent most of Sunday with me, expressed concern after reading it: 'Rod, are you sure these people are not going to come after you?'

I'd done my best to reassure her, pointing out that this was modern-day England not old-time Chicago, and in any case they wouldn't dare because any action would simply point the finger at who they are - and render them liable to prosecution by the police as well as by the BHA. She'd still looked doubtful.

'You off to Ludlow after this?' Paddy asked, after giving instructions to two of the lads about what work their horses were to do.

'Yes. What way do you go? Cirencester, Gloucester and Ledbury? Or up the M5 and tack across?'

Paddy pondered, silently rubbing his unshaven chin with his gloved hand.

'I haven't been since university, and it was an easy trip up the motorway to Kidderminster and then across'

Paddy, still thinking, answered: 'Jaysus. Probably not much between the M5 and across country. It's a bugger either way. Take you two and a half hours. What time's yer horse running?'

'He's in the second, 1.35. But I need to be there for the first.'

'Right, we'd better crack on. Brenda!'

The shout could be heard all over the yard. Heads turned and Brenda, wearing a red jersey this time, came hurrying up.

'Morning Rod,' she smiled.

'Brenda, get Halton ready will you? We've got to school him early.'

I went with her to the tack room and from there to the second last box where the white-blazed head was looking over the door, watching all the activity.

Between us we had him ready, led out and me legged up in little more than three minutes. I slotted into a gap between the increasing number circling. Brenda soon joined us, this time on a bright chestnut called, somewhat appropriately, Flash Harry. Unlike her mount the last time, though, this one was well-behaved.

'We'll lead,' she said. 'We're going up to High Down, do a canter and then you and I are going to school over three fences.'

I turned and counted ten other horses as we went up the path, with her chatting happily about horses and racing most of the way.

'Rod?' I looked round. It was a small, dark-haired lad on a grey. I had a feeling that his name was Jerry but I wasn't sure enough to address him as such. Instead I eased back so that his horse and mine were upsides.

"Ezekiel today, is he worth a few quid?'

I shook my head. "Two miles is too short and the horse needs the run. This is more to put him right for next time. When I'll be back.'

I didn't want to tell him that the horse wasn't trying but I knew he would be able to read between the lines.

'Billy Black is good value for his 5lb claim, though.' Seemingly Jerry hadn't got the message. 'He's on a roll at the moment, too, and 16-1 looks value.'

'Well,' I hesitated, not quite sure what to say next. The last thing I wanted was for him to lose his money. 'I can't see him winning.'

'Fair enough,' Jerry grinned. 'I'll wait until I see the great journalist down to ride him.'

'Hopefully.' I gave Halton Manor a nudge in the ribs and he moved back alongside Brenda's mount. When we reached the lone five-barred gate we circled, the horses becoming increasingly excited.

'OK Rod? You ready?' Brenda called out. 'We're going upsides. Just a canter.' Again we went two-by-two but this time with Halton Manor and Flash Harry in the lead. Both horses travelled well and seemed, to me at least, to be going well within themselves. The excitement of galloping, and the power of the horse I was riding, surged through me and I could almost feel the adrenaline pumping into my veins. No injection needed - I was as high as a kite.

We eased down as we neared the maroon Discovery and the driver standing beside it, binoculars hanging from the strap around his neck. 'OK Rod? OK Brenda?'

He didn't wait for an answer. 'Now Brenda, walk to the schooling ground, go to the far end and come back over all three fences at a decent pace. Sensible, mind. I don't want any mishaps.'

'Yes guv'nor,' she acknowledged, touching the peak of her helmet's red cap as she did so.

I moved my horse up alongside hers as we left the others and walked away to the right, up a slight slope. When we reached the top I saw, laid out in front of us, three racecourse fences and alongside each one a set of hurdles. The fences, as I realised when we got closer, were much smaller than the four feet-plus of those on the course.

We walked past all three and kept going for another fifty yards. 'Horses jump better if they are heading for home,' my companion pointed out. I already knew this but I was impressed by Brenda's knowledge and understanding of horses.

When we turned, both horses broke into a gallop and headed fast towards the fences. Too fast. I had to steady mine and Flash Harry was shouted at to do the same: 'Slow down, you stupid bugger.'

The horse got the message. We were travelling at a much more sensible pace by the time they both picked up stride going into the first of the three and took off. Halton Manor, I was pleased to see, jumped the fence cleanly and landed running. Flash Harry, on the other hand, took it high and cleared the obstacle with over a foot to spare.

We galloped on towards the next and Brenda allowed her mount to go a length up as we went into it. I knew exactly what she was doing. Some horses, particularly inexperienced ones, tend to take off when the horse next to them does so, and in a race they can find themselves crashing into the top of the fence because they took off too far away from it.

But Halton Manor was an old hand, too wise and too experienced to fall for that trick. He took off on the right stride, jumped the fence cleanly and landed running. He did the same at the third and final fence, and we gradually slowed as we reached the pull-up where the Discovery was now parked.

'He was brilliant. Didn't put a foot wrong,' I breathlessly informed the grinning trainer, hoping he hadn't detected my lack of fitness. I'd been a bit lazy about the running in recent days. I'd have to resume in earnest tomorrow.

'Should we go again, guv?' asked Brenda as she came alongside me. 'Flash was jumping far too big.'

'Jaysus, Brenda. Did yerself think you was at the Horse of the Year show or sumtin?' Seemingly Paddy thought it was the rider's fault. 'You looked as if you was jumpin' Bechers.'

'That's why he needs to go again, guv.'

Paddy shook his head. 'The Manor was good. Got on well with Rod too, and that was the object of the exercise. We'll go again with Harry later in the week. Back to the stables now. Just walk them to let them cool down.'

He turned to me and glanced at his watch. 'It's only just gone nine. You've got plenty of time. Don't forget to drop in on Mary before you head off. See you at Exeter on Friday.'

It was nearly half past by the time I tossed my helmet and whip into the boot of the car, and I was opening the driver's side door when I heard: 'Hi Rod, breakfast's ready.'

I'd planned to buy a roll when I was much further into the journey, but I felt I couldn't refuse. Paddy had been so good to me that a bad report from an annoyed wife would seem like an ungrateful kick in the teeth.

'I know you're in a hurry but you need a good breakfast inside you to keep you going,' she said as she placed a plate of bacon, eggs, mushrooms and fried bread in front of me and promptly added a cup of tea. I calculated that the extra ten minutes would be offset by the time I would save on not having to search for somewhere selling a breakfast roll. I tried not to rush the eating as Mary prattled on about the weather ('lot of rain later in the week'), the government ('what are they going to put up next?') and last night's TV programmes ('Did you see what that woman Carol said? Deserved all she got, I say').

I stood up, thanked her for 'a fantastic breakfast' – which it was – and apologised for having to rush off. She accompanied me to the car where I gave her a grateful peck on the cheek, followed by a wave as I reversed and then headed off through the now-open metal gate.

Five miles down the road I turned left into a lane and soon found what I was looking for. The grass-covered area in front of a gate into a field full of cows seemed firm enough for me to pull in, with enough of the car off the lane to let others pass. I quickly took trousers and shoes out of the grip, whipped off my jodhpurs and boots, and changed into racegoing gear. I calculated that I'd lost no more than six minutes by the time I turned the car and headed back down the lane.

The road bypassing Swindon and Cirencester was busy but fast. Going down the steep Birdlip hill I debated whether to make for the M5 or go round Gloucester to head for Ledbury.

Then I remembered a trip to Worcester when there had been an accident, and such a long tailback, that I was delayed twenty minutes and nearly missed the first. I couldn't afford that so I took the A 417. Staunton, over the M50, bypassing Ledbury, but Newtown was slow and the traffic seemed to crawl each side of Leominster. I kept looking at the dashboard clock as the minutes ticked away like the countdown to an unexploded bomb.

At last I got there and, as I drove into the car park, there was just ten minutes before the first race. I grabbed my laptop out of the boot and hurried to the press room. There were three other scribes already there, all sitting at the table and watching the horses going down to the start on TV. The *Racing Post*'s Tom Cameron, red-haired, fortyish and ever-curious, I already knew and the other two turned out to be local reporters. Barbara - seemingly slightly younger than Tom but grey hairs already showing among the black – was, she explained, covering the social scene while John was doing the racing. He looked barely old enough to have left school but had plenty to say for himself and seemed to know it all. I took an immediate dislike.

'Ezekiel in with a chance, I thought?' Tom fished.

'Hmm, too short really.' I certainly didn't want to tell the

Racing Post the horse was not off. 'Needs the run anyway.'

'Guess so. Just thought that with Black riding so well he might just go off in front and try to slip the field.'

'He's well in at the weights and better value than the current 10-1,' John chipped in. 'Wouldn't surprise me if he won – particularly with a jockey riding this time.'

Annoyance bursting within me, I ignored the insult and headed off to the weighing room in search of Trevor. I found Willie Monaghan. The travelling head lad was talking to Billy Black. Both men looked up as I joined them and said 'Hi Rod' almost in unison.

'Trevor here?'

'No, he's not coming today," Willie replied, his Irish roots still evident in his accent even though I knew he'd been in England for over fifteen years. 'Just the one runner so I guess he tought it wasn't worth it.'

Logical - but he should at least have phoned me to say he wasn't coming. I was the owner, after all, and the one paying his not inconsiderable bills – and paying them promptly, unlike some of the other owners. Sarah had told me that the late payers were a major problem.

'Orse has been workin' quite well, particularly t' last few days,' said Willie.

'Bit short, though,' added Billy, smiling cheerfully as he handed over his saddle. 'Still, this should set him up nicely for you, Rod.'

Back in the press room I watched the finishing stages of the first race, sorted out my notes, checked who I wanted to speak to and, just as I was leaving to head for the parade

144

ring, I heard John saying: 'Looks like I was right. He's down to 10-1 now.'

I looked at the odds of the leading contenders superimposed on the screen. Ezekiel, having opened at 12-1, was now among the 10-1 chances. When I looked again he was 8-1.

In the parade ring - unusually it was more of a square that the traditional oval - fifteen minutes later Billy, arms folded and flexing his toes and knees, was talking about nothing very much to Willie who was casting his eyes over the other runners as all twelve circled the ring, blankets still on and most showing little sign of excitement. The wind was bitingly cold and I regretted not having thought to bring my overcoat in the rush to leave the flat.

The bell rang. All three of us walked over to Ezekiel who had been brought to a halt by Manch Wilkinson. Willie wordlessly legged Billy into the saddle and the jockey began knotting his reins as Manch led the horse off round the ring. Willie headed towards the stands while I went in the other direction to where the horses were going through the exit rails and onto the course.

Manch turned after releasing the horse, saw me and came over. 'Should run well,' he said, smiling. 'Been working well.'

'Not too well, I hope. We don't want him winning and getting a penalty for next time.'

Manch shook his head. 'The guv'nor told me not to back him. Said it would be too short.'

I went back to the press room via the bookmakers. '4-1 now,' I heard one of them call out. 'Back this good thing before he gets any shorter.'

I looked in astonishment as I went down the line. Some

bookmakers even had Ezekiel at 7-2 and a few at 3-1.

'Going for a touch, Rod?' enquired one in a voice that was vaguely familiar. I looked up at the pork pie hat and the 'Best prices since 1996' board. I shook my head, almost in horror. 'I know The Major tipped him,' Jack Joseph continued. 'But I didn't expect money like this. Nobody wants to know any of the others.'

My return to the press room was greeted with an embarrassed silence. John, Barbara and Tom looked at each other, smiled and said nothing. Clearly I'd been the subject of conversation.

Predictably it was John who spoke first. 'Reckon you've got it wrong, Rod. Ezekiel's been backed as if there's no tomorrow. Be a major shock if he doesn't win.'

I shrugged my shoulders and pretended to be searching for something in my notebook, flicking over the pages one by one.

'I hope John's right,' said Barbara. 'I've put a tenner on.'

'At 8-1,' added John with a smug note of satisfaction. 'I've got a score on at tens.'

'I hardly ever bet but ..... so much money going on,' said Tom slowly. 'I couldn't resist it. I'll collect a hundred quid if he wins.'

'They're off,' shouted the voice from the TV, fortunately putting further betting details on hold. I watched my white, blue sleeves and hooped cap settle in fifth as the ten runners headed towards the first fence at a far from exacting pace. Good. I knew Ezekiel's best chance, over a trip too short for him, would be if they went at a strong gallop – and, after what I'd told everybody, he had to lose. Otherwise I would be regarded as a crook - or worse.

He took the fences cleanly as they came up the straight, turned sharply right and then headed off down the back straight. After jumping the last of the four fences there, an open ditch, Ezekiel moved up and he was in front as the horses turned for home. I was pleased to see Billy go for his whip – clearly Ezekiel was running out of steam. But, far from tiring, the horse seemed to find another gear and he increased his advantage.

'Go on, you good thing,' yelled John as his investment soared over the next.

Barbara was also on her feet. 'I can hardly bear to watch,' she whispered, her clenched fists barely covering her eyes. Even the taciturn Tom was standing up, muttering 'Come on, you beauty.'

Ezekiel was tiring as he approached the final fence, his advantage halved from ten lengths to five. 'Please God, make him fall,' I silently prayed. But seemingly the Almighty was not much bothered about the 1.35pm at Ludlow. Ezekiel jumped it cleanly and it was his nearest pursuer who fell.

Barbara hugged her equally delighted local journalist and Tom, beaming from ear to ear, thrust out a hand in congratulation. I shook it briefly before heading for the winner's enclosure, knowing just what people mean when they talk about wishing the earth would open up and swallow them.

I was sickened, mortified and furious. Apart from anything else, I'd been made to look a fool. I reached the winner's enclosure as Billy rode into it. He looked at me, touched his cap and grinned. 'Well done,' he said as he slipped his feet out of the irons and himself off the horse. He was still smiling broadly as he unbuckled the girth, pulled off the saddle and headed to the weighing room to stand on the scales.

'That was fecking grand,' said Willie Monaghan before seeing my face and, presumably, recalling that I hadn't wanted the horse to win. The travelling head lad said nothing more as Manch led the horse away with Willie following closely.

It was only then that I realised some of the crowd were angry. There weren't that many around the winner's enclosure, no more than twenty. But they had plenty to say. 'Wouldn't have won with you on, you fucking tosser,' shouted a small man in a mac and flat cap.

'Yer didn't tip that one on yer effing website,' said his neighbour, a much larger figure in a Barbour.

'How much did you have on, eh?' shouted another. By this stage I wasn't seeing anything too clearly. I decided to get out and return to the comparative peace and quiet of the press room. As I turned on my heel I heard further shouts and insults. 'Calls himself a journalist, he's a fucking crook' echoed in my ears, now turning red along with the rest of my face.

I was glad to see John and Barbara were not in the room. Presumably they had gone to collect their winnings – or celebrate them. Tom stopped typing long enough to look up and say, with more than a hint of sympathy in his voice: 'I guess you've been stitched up – like a kipper.'

'I think you're right,' I said, slumping down beside him. 'It was agreed that the horse wouldn't be ridden to win, only to get him ready for me when I returned. And yet he's backed off the boards and wins by God knows how far.'

'Three lengths. Might not have won if the second horse hadn't fallen at the last,' pointed out the *Racing Post* man. 'He was catching yours hand over fist.'

'But he did fall. That's the problem.'

I decided to ring Trevor. But not from the press room. I went to the car and rang his mobile. I more than half expected he wouldn't answer. But seemingly he was expecting the call. After just two rings I heard: 'Well done, Rod. Horse has obviously improved since last season. You still OK for Bangor on Saturday? Brown River's in cracking form.'

'Trevor,' I said slowly and carefully. 'You told me the horse was only having a run to put him right for next time. Yet he wins by three lengths and, even worse, he's backed off the boards. You've made me look a fool and a crook.'

'Rod, I think you're being too hard on yourself.' I got the impression that Trevor had prepared himself for my comments, and had worked out the answers to any awkward questions. 'The Major tipped him. What did you expect? He's on fire.'

'OK,' I said slowly, wondering about this. I hadn't had time to read Charles's column. 'See you on Saturday.'

Back in the press room I logged on to *sports-all.com*'s racing pages. 'Go into battle with The Major' was emblazoned across the tipping piece. 'Our man has won with ten of his last sixteen tips. Profit of £175.60 to £10 level stake so far this month.'

Towards the bottom of the Ludlow section Charles had written: 'Ezekiel could be worth a chance in the second despite this being his first race of the season. He won first time out two years ago and, with his enthusiastic amateur owner sidelined, rising star Billy Black takes over. Black, a future champion, claims 5lb but is as good as any of the top professionals. His claim means that he has five lengths in hand. True, the trip is on the short side, but Black can compensate for that.'

'Know who backed him?' John was reading the article over my shoulder. He didn't wait for an answer. 'Jimmy Brownson, Trevor's brother.'

'The man who's been spending all that money on yearlings?' Tom looked up from his typing, his attention switching sharply at John's words.

'None other. He likes a bet and he bets big. Wouldn't be the first time the stable has pulled a stroke like this.'

'What's he do for a living?' Seemingly Tom was still curious.

'Some sort of investment banker, I think,' John answered. 'Got his finger in a lot of pies.'

At least little Mr Know-all wasn't right about everything. Further discussion was brought to a halt by the start of the next. Billy Black won the race on The Major's third and final tip of the day - he'd also tipped the first race winner. I looked up the betting returns. The opening winner had been backed from 4-1 to 5-2 and the third one from 6-1 to 7-2. Significant, but possibly explainable by the tipster's winning run. Ezekiel, though, was not. He had shortened from 12-1 to 7-4. Maybe John was right.

After Billy completed a treble in the next race, his third and final ride of the day, I hurried into the weighing room to catch him before he left the course. 'He's in the shower,' said the white-coated attendant at the door to the jockeys' room. Two minutes later Billy appeared, wearing only a towel and a broad grin.

It was his third treble of the season, he was nineteen and had already been booked for leading fancy King Creole in the King George on Boxing Day. He rattled off further relevant newsworthy details – his ambition to be champion jockey and his injuries so far – four broken collar bones, three concussions and two dislocated shoulders – as if he was reading them from his own mental newspaper.

'Just going back to Ezekiel, Billy. What instructions did Trevor give you?'

Billy looked at me sharply - seemingly he knew what I was getting at. 'Just to ride him as I found him. To remember that it was his first race of the season, and not to knock him about.'

'And to win if you could?'

'Well, I took that as a given.' He grinned. 'But I knew you'd be back on next time, and I wanted to leave him right for you.'

Tactful. But if he was expecting a present from me – some owners added an extra ten per cent of the prize money to the percentage deducted at source – he was going to be disappointed.

I led my report with his treble and his quotes. I also quoted Trevor and spoke of my embarrassment after assuring people that Ezekiel couldn't win despite the wholesale gamble on him. I was careful to make no mention of Trevor's brother or the barracking in the winner's enclosure – I didn't want a wider audience to start thinking like that.

By the time I finished and checked all the facts it was nearly an hour after the last race. Myself and Tom, still typing away, were just about the only ones left on the racecourse. I packed my notepad and racecard into my laptop bag and headed out to the car park.

I was surprised how cold it had become. The dark sky was crystal clear and I could just about see my breath as I debated whether to go back the way I'd come, or go via Worcester and the M5. I fished in my pocket for the remote - and I was promptly smashed against the side of the car.

The man who gripped my right arm heaved me violently forward at the same time as the one who had taken hold of my other arm - and it was my mouth that took the full force of the impact, with my face crashing into the metalwork where the side of the car met the roof. The blow jolted through my head like a powerful surge of electricity, and it hurt like hell. I gingerly ran my tongue over my teeth. All I could taste was blood, and there seemed to be plenty of it.

I tried to tell my attackers they had got the wrong man, that I was a journalist not a bookmaker – and that my case contained my laptop, not the day's takings. But even to my ears the words were indecipherable.

It was only then that I realised there was a third man. I was heaved away from the car by the other two to face a big, powerful thug in a balaclava. His gloved fist crashed into my stomach with all the force of a pile-driver. I doubled up in agony as the pain made me gasp, or try to - all the air had been driven out of my lungs. I would have slumped to the ground had not the other two insisted on holding me upright. They too, I could now see, were also wearing gloves and balaclavas.

Not a word had been spoken by my attackers. The big man produced something out of the pocket of his leather jacket and I heard a click as he shook it. 'Hold him steady,' he said to the other two. The Brummie accent was even more pronounced than that of Jack Joseph's nephew Arnold.

Still gasping for breath, and still feeling the agonising pains in my stomach and mouth, I sensed the skin on my throat being cut – carefully and slowly – from one side of my neck to the other. I was terrified. 'Now, Mr 'utchinson. You lay off the bookmakers. Or next time this razor will cut so deep you won't write another word. Understand?'

The blade went in a fraction deeper, as if to emphasise his point. I could feel blood oozing down into my collar. 'OK,' I spluttered, not daring to nod in case the razor cut again.

The man who held my right arm in a vice-like grip muttered something that sounded like 'The best,' and was rewarded with a fierce 'Shut up, Jake' for his troubles.

'Over there with him,' commanded the big man and I was marched about fifteen yards away. The other two still held me tightly as the big man walked purposely towards me and, with a sudden horror, I realised what was coming. He drew his fist back, and I screamed as he let fly at my stomach once more. The pain was even worse than the first time. The whole target area was now horribly sore and I again doubled up as I slumped to the ground, coughing and retching. All three men were walking away as the sandwich I'd eaten for lunch came up with what was left of Mary's breakfast. It smelled revolting as I coughed and spluttered into the grass in front of my face.

After a few minutes I tried to get to my feet. I struggled to push myself up with my hands. The pain in my stomach intensified beyond belief and I crumpled in agony, my face splashing into the pool of sick. The stench was disgusting. But I hadn't even the strength to move my head.

Soon I could sense it was getting even colder. At least I was, and I began to shiver. I knew I had to try again. If I stayed where I was I could freeze to death. I summoned every last ounce of strength. Somehow my hands pushed and my body lifted. But my legs were numb. They gave way at the knees and I fell heavily. Again my face landed in the sick. And the pain in my stomach was unbearable. It was like a dagger being twisted inside me. It was tearing me apart. I began to sob. I couldn't stop crying.

'Please God, don't let me die,' I prayed. The cold numbed my hands. I tried again to get up. My legs wouldn't respond. And I was shivering uncontrollably. I wondered how long it would be before the life departed from me. The intense cold was proving too strong for my will to live. I thought back to that old story of how your whole life passes in front of you in your dying minutes. I tried to focus on the best bits: my first winner ..... Emma .....I thought back to other girlfriends. But I couldn't focus on anything except the pain and the cold.

11

I knew I was passing into unconsciousness when I saw a faint light. Was this the other side? The light was flickering and doing a criss-cross waving as if its owner was searching for something. I tried to shout but all that came out was a croak, and even that sent the pain ratcheting through me once more. I knew I couldn't call out a second time.

The light suddenly changed direction and pointed my way. 'Good God.' It was Tom Cameron. I prayed again. 'Please God, let him see me.'

He came close, the light from his phone making me blink as he shone it into my face. 'Rod, is that you?'

I croaked. Not a word came out.

'Can you get up?' he reached out with his right hand, grabbed mine and heaved me to my feet. I staggered almost upright, my legs gave way and I fell heavily, bringing him down with me. I clutched my stomach in an almost futile bid to ease the pain as he got to his feet.

'Come on, Rod. For God's sake,' he shouted. 'You've got to get up.'

This time I did manage it. I held on to his arm, gasping for breath as he tried to disengage himself. He pulled me towards my car, went through my pockets, found the remote, opened the door and pushed me onto the driver's seat. With some difficulty, he managed to get the key into the ignition and switch on the engine.

He went round the other side, got into the passenger seat and reached across to put the heater on boost. His nose wrinkling at the smell, he said: 'What the hell happened?'

'Got mugged,' I managed. 'They must have thought I was a bookie with a pile of cash.'

'Hang on,' he said, getting out of the car and shutting the door behind him. He disappeared round the back before opening the door on my side. He had my laptop case with him. "They didn't take this anyway. I'm putting it in the boot.'

I heard the boot open and being slammed shut. 'Are you going to be able to drive home?' he asked after opening the driver's side door once more. 'I could call for an ambulance?'

I shook my head. The warmth flooding through me was having a miraculous effect. 'I'll be OK in a few minutes.'

'Thank God. Listen Rod, I'm going to have to go.' He made a show of looking at his watch. 'I should have been home an hour ago but Sedgefield's been frozen off and the *Post* wanted a second preview for Southwell .' He peered closely. 'Your face is in one hell of a mess. Blood everywhere. They must have really worked you over.'

'You head off Tom. I'll just sit in the car for five minutes. Then I'll be away too. I'll grab something to eat somewhere. That 'll help.'

'Did they take your phone?'

I felt in my trouser pocket. It was still there. I gave him a thumbs up.

'Thank goodness you weren't one of the bookies. They would probably have killed you.' Tom got into his car, switched on the ignition and the lights, gave a wave and was gone.

I didn't dare wait any longer - my attackers might be still around – and I was on my way within three minutes. I decided to go the same way as I came. I didn't want to risk going wrong on a strange road to the motorway, particularly in the dark.

But as I neared Ledbury I could hardly keep my eyes open. I decide I would have to look for a hotel for the night and went into the town. As I pulled up outside the Tudor-fronted Feathers Hotel I wondered about the price – it looked horribly expensive. Then I caught sight of my face in the mirror. It was lit up by a street light and looked like something out of a horror movie. My mouth was swollen, and my chin and left cheek were caked in blood. There was more dried blood on both sides of my throat.

The shock woke up my senses. I had to go on – and I now felt I could. What I needed was black coffee. Salvation proved to be a mobile chip van on the outskirts of the town. Doing my best to cover my face from the attendant's gaze, I bought a bag of chips, a bottle of Coca Cola, and coffee in a paper cup. Half a mile up the road I consumed my meal

– thankfully my stomach made no objection despite the beating it had received – and I was ready for the hundred miles or so to home.

As I lay in the bath, my stomach a mixture of black bruises and still-painful red soreness, I pondered about the motives of my attackers – and whoever had sent them to beat me up. 'Lay off the bookmakers,' the big thug had warned. But which ones? And why? And what particular article had upset them so much that they had resorted to such violence.? True, journalists did sometimes come under attack but print and verbal retaliation was the norm, not physical attacks or threats with a knife.

My article on *weRthebestbets.com* was harmless enough, surely? True, it contained some derogatory comments from rivals, but the general gist was that the online-only bookie was good for punters. The electric whips feature was a different matter, though, with unscrupulous trainers accused of making arrangements with certain bookmakers to get over the odds in return for information. The jigger twins had already revealed a fondness for using knives - admittedly only on my car tyres – but there was that note: 'Next time it won't be just your tyres that get slashed.' And, if Paddy O'Reilly's information was correct, the *weRthebestbets.com* owner was up to his neck in the whole fraud.

And Jake had said something about the best. Did he mean *weRthebestbets.com*? I searched my memory for his exact words but the accent was so strong that I couldn't be sure what it was he had actually said.

Also Sarah had warned that I was in serious danger, and to watch out for an attack, particularly in a racecourse car park. How did she get this information? More than feminine intuition, she'd said, something she'd heard. But who from?

Then there was Charles's warning: 'Keep your nose out or you'll get knifed.' Prophetic words, or advice from somebody who knew how these particular thugs operate?

Half an hour of confusing and contradictory speculation later I heaved myself out of the water – at least the hot soak should have helped my battered stomach muscles – and looked in the mirror. The marks left by the cut-throat razor were slight – only about an inch long on either side – but my mouth was a red mass of swollen skin and still painful to the touch.

I dried myself, put on my pyjamas and dressing gown, poured myself a large brandy and sat down to ring Emma. She was predictably horrified, even though I only gave her a watered-down version, leaving out both the threats and the razor. She suggested coming over and spending the night with me. I realised how tired I was, and the effect the brandy was having, and declined an offer that I would have almost died for at any other time in our still-brief relationship.

Thanks in no small part to the brandy I slept like a log. The bedside clock showed 7.40 am when I woke. Deliberately avoiding looking in any mirrors, I made myself a cup of tea and pulled back all the curtains to let in another grey day. My phone rang. It was Brett. Not like him to ring so early.

'You OK?' He didn't sound particularly concerned. And he didn't wait for an answer. 'Rodney, you've let us down badly. One of the biggest racing stories of the year. Plastered all over the front of the *Racing Post*. And what have we got?

Fuck all. Except you're embarrassed because your horse wins.'

'Sorry Brett. I was in a bad way. Much as I could do to drive home.'

'All you had to do was pick up the phone.' He was still spitting blood. 'We could have pieced it together from here. At least we would have had a story. And we would have had it first instead of being turned into an industry laughing-stock.'

'Sorry Brett,' I repeated, conscious that I sounded far from convincing. I was beginning to see his point.

'Now, I want you to write the story we should have had. But with a lot more detail than the *Post*. What the muggers said to you. How they threatened you. How they beat you up. Who you think it was. And why. All the details. And I want it by 10.00am. OK?'

'Yes, will do. But if ....'

He cut me off. 'Just write the story and send it to me personally. Anything you still haven't covered by 10.00am we'll use for the follow-up. I'll want a follow-up anyway. Possibly several. This story could run and run.'

He disconnected before I could say anything else. I went to the door of the flat, and the pile of papers that had come through the letter box. I spent a fortune on newspapers, and seldom read anything except the racing pages. As a journalist I had to know what was news, and what wasn't. The *Racing Post* was the only one I really read in any detail. I picked it up to be hit by a front-page picture of me falling at Sandown under the banner headline: RACING JOURNALIST ATTACKED AT LUDLOW AFTER EZEKIEL LANDS MASSIVE GAMBLE.

Tom Cameron described finding me lying in the grass and clutching my stomach at the edge of the car park, unable to get up, in agony and my face covered in blood. He quoted me as saying my attackers must have mistaken me for a bookmaker thinking my laptop bag contained the day's takings. He commented on the fact that the muggers, curiously, had not gone off with either the laptop or my phone. He suggested that the attack was linked to the gamble on Ezekiel, and that some disgruntled punters had decided to administer 'justice.' He also quoted some of the insults directed at me in the winner's enclosure. Clearly he had not, as I'd thought, been in the press room at the time.

I sat down at the computer on the table beside my desk and wrote my version. I didn't need to map out this one in advance. The whole thing was fresh in my mind, and I was bursting to start even while reading the *Racing Post*. I began with the knife blade on my throat and the warning to 'lay off the bookmakers or next time this razor will go in so deep you won't write another word.'

I continued with the beating, the damage to my stomach and mouth, and recapped on the electric whips article - with particular reference to those responsible getting their money on over the odds with certain bookmakers, in return for the information that the horses couldn't lose. It was this article, I suggested, that had led to the vicious attack.

I looked at my watch. Just gone 9.00am, plenty of time left for me to check it all before filing. Then my phone started ringing. First it was Paddy O'Reilly asking how I was and whether I was still OK for Friday, then a couple of other journalists expressing sympathy. As I disconnected after the second one, I saw the message: 'Couldn't get through. Please ring. Sarah.'

'Oh Rod,' she cried when she answered. 'Are you alright?' She sounded as if she was fighting back tears. Before I could answer she went on: 'This is exactly what I feared. Didn't you listen to what I said that night at the Regency Park?'

'Sarah, I'm OK,' I tried to reassure her. 'Just a few bruises. I'll be as right as rain in a couple of days.'

'Rod, please be careful,' she implored, more than a trace of desperation in her voice. 'Particularly in racecourse car parks after dark. Get one of the other journalists, or somebody, to go with you when you leave.'

'Sarah, just listen to me. You told me about the dangers of the car parks. Who told you this was going to happen?'

She sniffed tearfully. 'Nobody told me. I just heard somebody saying something – I can't remember the exact words – but the gist was that there were people who wanted to silence you. And I knew how vulnerable you could be leaving the press room in the dark. Please be careful, Rod. I think they might try again.'

'So it wasn't anybody specific?'

'No. Just something I heard.'

'And Sarah. Last Saturday at Ascot, when I went into the restaurant, you turned away as if you didn't want to speak to me. Why?'

'It was Margaret.' I could hear the amusement in her voice. I was glad she was back in a more cheerful frame of my mind. 'She thinks we're having an affair. Somebody saw us leaving that conference room at the Regency Park, and told her.'

I remembered the girl in the long dress hurrying down the stairs.

'That's why I left the note on your windscreen. Hope you weren't offended.'

We talked for another five minutes. But I had to get back to the article. I'd be in more trouble if I didn't get it in by ten. She made me promise not to leave any racecourse in the dark on my own from now on. It wasn't a difficult promise to make.

I saved her number for future use before reading the piece through once more. I made a few minor changes, read it again, this time checking all the facts. It was 9.30 am when I sent it. Fifteen minutes later there was an email from Brett: 'Perfect. Don't forget the follow-ups, tomorrow at the latest.'

A plate of cereal later it was on the website. And on the front page. I smiled. Brett might be a master of the latest technology but he was also a firm believer in the old newspaper dictum: if it bleeds, it leads.

'Our man threatened at knife point. A bookmaker responsible?' was the headline. I read it through. Brett had changed almost nothing. But the usual feeling of satisfaction at reading what I knew to be a good piece was missing. All I could think of was how George Rickards was going to react. Would the *weRthebestbets.com* owner really get his strong-arm guys to cut my throat?

I shivered. I feared I already knew the answer.

The phone started ringing again - before I'd even had a chance to get dressed or shaved. The Ludlow racecourse manager wanted to apologise, said he had spoken to the caretaker who would not leave the course until everyone had gone in future, and that he had reported the attack to the police. They would be in touch because they viewed 'the incident' (as he called it) every bit as seriously as he did, and he had given them my number.

Emma said she was coming to the flat after the surgery closed at 6.00pm, she would be bringing our supper, she would stay to cook it and this time she wasn't taking no for an answer.

John Jameson was next on the line. The chairman had asked him to do a report on security for the press at all UK racecourses as a matter of urgency - and to recommend what measures needed to be taken to ensure the Ludlow incident didn't happen to anyone else. Jameson wanted to know which courses had inadequate lighting between the press rooms and the car parks. He seemed unimpressed by my off-the-cuff answer of 'pretty well all of them.' But he must have known it was true from his journalistic days.

I'd started shaving – the bruising round my mouth was a lot less than the night before but still sore – when a Welsh-accent announced itself as Detective-Sergeant Dai Jones of West Mercia Police investigating 'your knife attack at the racecourse yesterday evening.' He was coming to see me and would be in Reading around 2.00pm. What was my home address?

I looked at my watch while I inspected my stomach. It was just gone 11.30am, some of the bruising had gone from red to black and was outlined in an unpleasant-looking shade of yellow. The whole area was extremely tender, so much so that I gave up my plan to go for a run to help get me fit for Friday.

I looked again at my website piece and this time I read through the twenty or so comments that now appeared below it. Most of them expressed sympathy, or disgust, at what had happened but half a dozen of them hit out at the improved form of Ezekiel, seemed to think I was responsible and deserved all I got.

Detective-Sergeant Jones arrived as I was finishing my sandwich lunch. Tall and thin, he was in plain clothes and only looked about my age. Taking a seat at the kitchen table, and declining my offer of a cup of coffee or tea, he asked a succession of questions. What did my attackers look like, how old were they, had I seen them before, had I ever been attacked like this, had I heard of anybody else being attacked at Ludlow racecourse, or at any course anywhere else, why did I think I was attacked? He had a notebook in front of him but he wrote down surprisingly little.

'I read your article before ringing you this morning and again about half an hour ago,' he said, his tone changing slightly. 'A number of the comment writers seemed to suggest you had been less than honest with the public and made a lot of money betting on your horse.'

'That's balls. At least it is so far as me personally is concerned. I didn't have a penny on him.'

'Why not?' The detective seemed unimpressed and unbelieving. 'Everybody else at the racecourse yesterday seems to have done so.'

I explained how I normally rode my horses myself and that this run was intended to put Ezekiel right for when I next rode him. Instead he was going to go up in the handicap, making success next time far from likely.

'So it was the trainer who pulled a fast one?' Dai Jones, seemingly, knew a little more about racing that he had let on.

'It would appear that way,' I answered slowly and carefully. I didn't want to go down this road - I had no evidence and I didn't want him turning up at Trevor's stables, confronting the trainer with accusations from me.

'Just go back to when you left the press room and tell me what happened.'

I ran through everything. He made the odd brief note, but said nothing until I reached the point where Tom Cameron helped me to my feet.

'These three men? What did they look like? Would you be able to recognise them again?'

I explained about the balaclavas but remembered the Birmingham accents and that one of the two men holding my arms was called Jake.

'Ah,' said the detective, writing something down. 'We know a bit about the three men but the name Jake is a step forward.'

'You mean you know who they are?'

'Not enough to identify them. But yours is the fourth attack like this so far this year. The others weren't on racecourses but the beatings and the knife threats were much the same. We suspect the men are some sort of rent-a-thugs from the Birmingham area.'

'So what are you going to do about them? And what are you going to do about finding who their paymasters are?'

Dai Jones folded up his notebook, got to his feet and

smiled. 'Thank you, Mr Hutchinson. You have been most helpful. We may need to talk to you again.'

I accompanied him as far as the door, shook his hand and asked him to keep me informed of developments. He didn't answer.

I went to the computer and typed out as much of his actual words as I could remember before writing an update for Brett, centred on the racecourse press security review ordered by the BHA chairman and the measures being taken at Ludlow to prevent the possibility of any further attacks.

I filed it with a note about the police visit which, I said, would go into the next update and be filed at 10.00am the following morning. Other journalists might come up with some of today's update but they wouldn't know the details of the police visit, I explained, so that would still be news in the morning.

'Agreed,' Brett replied ten minutes later. 'What's your plans for the rest of the week?'

I filed back: 'Wednesday, Thursday: office at home. Friday: Exeter to ride Halton Manor and report, Saturday: Bangor-on-Dee to ride Brown River and report.'

'Noted,' came the acknowledgement, almost immediately.

I would need to be well clear of the racecourses, *and their approach roads*, before it got dark. I couldn't rely on George Rickards sticking to the same modus operandi next time.

It was just after 6.30pm when Emma arrived, handbag in one hand and shopping in the other. She kissed me on the lips as she came in through the door, noticed me wince and said: 'Sorry, I can see I am going to have to be gentle with you.'

As she took off her coat and draped it over the back of the sofa I realised she was wearing the same sexy, tight-fitting black trousers as when I first met her in the surgery that Saturday morning. Only this time she had on a red silk blouse in place of the white polo neck. She looked sensational, and I said so.

'Thank you, Rod,' she answered as she unloaded the contents of the shopping bag into the fridge. 'I felt I had to make an impression after you turned down the offer of my body last night.'

'It wasn't like that.' I pulled her into my arms, and held her tight while my hands gently rubbed her bottom.

She chuckled. 'Thought that might get you.' She gently pushed me away. 'Better let me get on with the supper before I become too comfortable.'

Supper consisted of steak and kidney pie, potatoes and mixed vegetables, bought frozen and all heated up in twenty minutes while we had a drink – beer for me and a gin and tonic for Emma – followed by raspberries and ice cream.

'Are you still riding on Friday?' she asked as we started eating.

'Yes – and I'm feeling fine for that.' I thought she might be trying to stop me. I was wrong.

'Great,' she enthused. 'Can I come with you?'

'Sure – but aren't you working that day?'

'Not necessarily.' She smiled in a way that made me feel my heart was melting. 'Barbara, that's the agency girl who comes in on Thursdays, says she can switch to Friday. I said I would confirm with her in the morning.'

At the end of the meal, as we loaded the dishwasher, our heads touched. Emma looked up and smiled. 'Fancy coffee?' she asked.

'I fancy you more,' I replied, reaching out and pulling her towards the sofa. We sank down into it, locked in a passionate embrace. My right hand went round her left breast as I felt, and massaged, the nipple through the blouse and her bra. She gasped, passion and delight seemingly in equal proportions. I undid the buttons on her blouse one by one and, when I began to pull it off her shoulders, she wriggled free from it. We kissed again, this time long and searchingly, as I reached behind for her bra strap and unclipped it

'You seem rather good at that,' she whispered. 'I think you've had plenty of practice. Too much practice.' Her lips resumed contact with mine, and our tongues sought each other's. Mine moved to her left breast and caressed it before I began taking as much of it as I could into my mouth, while my tongue caressed the nipple.

'Oh Rod,' she gasped as I transferred my attentions to her other breast. Her response was to hold me even tighter. After several enjoyable minutes – I'm not sure who was the most turned on, her or me – my right hand went to the front of her trousers and fumbled with the catch.

'What are you doing? She whispered into my ear, giving the lobe a deliberately sharp and painful bite. 'You're a naughty boy.'

'I want to take your trousers off.'

'I only do that when it's time for bed.'

'It's time for bed now,' I replied pulling her to her feet and, with my right hand in her left, leading her towards the bedroom. It was at the back of the house, the curtains were open and there was enough light coming from outside for her to see the double bed and me to see her slipping out of her trousers. As I pulled back the duvet, she whispered 'Take your clothes off, my darling.'

I needed no second bidding and removed everything in record time. I saw she still had her panties on as we climbed into bed, and I resumed the caressing and kissing of her twin orbs of delight. Soon my hands went down to the panties. She lifted her bottom to enable me to slip them off.

She gasped again as my lips traversed a slow and tantalising path down her body and between her legs which opened as my tongue found its target. She was already wet.

'Do we need anything?' I hadn't forgotten about a contraceptive and I had a packet in the bedside table.

'What do you mean?' she whispered and then, before I had a chance to answer, she seemed to understand. 'No, I'm on the pill.'

My tongue caressed one side of the entrance, and then all round it, until it found what I was looking for. I took the button-like pleasure spot between my lips and felt her shudder as I sucked on it.

Her right hand reached for my erect penis. It was my turn to gasp as she grabbed it. 'Put it inside me, my darling,' she commanded breathlessly.

She cried out as I entered her and began moving slowly up and down. After about a minute of what was sheer pleasure for both of us I felt her tense. 'Oh Rod, darling,' she shuddered as her climax erupted. She bit hard into my shoulder. 'Now come,' she commanded breathlessly. 'I want to feel you come.'

I needed no second bidding. The ecstasy was indescribable and, quite literally, it took my breath away. For the best part of five minutes neither of us moved or even spoke, seemingly emptied of all energy.

Ten minutes later, though, with the curtains now pulled right across and the light on, we were both sitting up sipping at fridge-cool glasses of Coca Cola. Emma looked closely at my neck. 'Those marks are not as bad as I thought they would be. Probably be almost undetectable in a week or two, and my man will be just as handsome as before.'

'Stomach's still pretty bruised though.'

'Let's have a look.' She lifted the sheet and winced. The area of bruising was definitely less than 24 hours earlier, but more of the black had turned to dark yellow and there was still quite a lot of redness.

'Would it help if I massaged it gently?' Her right hand began a circular caressing movement. I didn't know if it was easing the bruising but it was certainly having an effect on another part of my anatomy.

'Why don't you stay the night?' I put my hand over hers to call a halt to the eroticism of her ministrations.

'Thought you would never ask. But I'll need my nightie and clothes for the morning.'

'I think we can dispense with the nightie,' I murmured. 'And you can use today's clothes when you go to work, can't you?'

'Uh uh,' she disagreed. 'If I turn up wearing the same clothes everyone will know I haven't been home all night.'

'OK. 'You'd better tell me what you want me to bring, and where I find them.' I wasn't exactly relishing swapping my present comfortable position for a trip to Tilehurst, even if it was only a few miles away.

'You'll find everything I need outside garage C downstairs, in my overnight bag in the boot of my car.'

I smiled, partly because I didn't now have to make the journey, but also because Emma had succeeded in winding me up - yet again. Would I ever learn to realise when she was having me on?

'Well, I didn't want to appear presumptuous by arriving with an overnight bag. Not after you rejected my body yesterday evening.'

I put on my dressing-gown and went down to the car with Emma urging me to be careful in case there was an attacker lying in wait. As I took the bag out of the boot, and relocked the car, I could see her looking out of the first floor window.

It was another hour before we returned to bed, and the second love-making was every bit as exciting and passionate as the first. We slept with her body pressed into mine and with my arms around her.

The following morning, though, it was all a bit of a rush with a flustered Emma pointing out that she had the busy roads to contend with before getting to the surgery by 8.30am.

I sat down and wrote the update, mostly about what Dai Jones had said – he wasn't going to be best pleased at seeing his quotes in print, particularly about the Birmingham rent-a-thugs and this being their fourth attack so far this year – but, hell, he had been speaking to a journalist. In any case I had a story to write, not to mention a boss who wanted to make the most of one of his reporters being so sensationally attacked.

I read it through, and I wasn't happy. No bite. I had to give it some teeth. I added an extra paragraph: 'The detective-sergeant didn't say anything to suggest the police know who is behind the attack. However I remain convinced that it is a particular bookmaking firm. I still don't know which one but, the more I think about it, the more I am convinced that my article on the electric whips scandal was the blue touch paper that led to the attack. Why else would the big thug warn me to "lay off the bookmakers?" '

Running along Thames Path an hour or so later – I was pleased to find that strenuous exercise was paining my battered stomach muscles so little – I thought about Friday's race and decided I must study the reruns of Halton Manor's recent races.

They proved to have a common theme - and it was hardly encouraging. He was invariably well placed, anywhere between third and sixth, and not far behind the leaders, and was given every chance. But, when the tap was turned on, he tended to drop back as the main contenders quickened. He was, not to put too fine a point on it, one-paced – a fatal flaw in any racehorse's make-up. I noticed that his best performances tended to be when the going was soft. Presumably because the testing ground blunted the acceleration of his rivals. But he hadn't won a race for two years despite dropping down the handicap.

On Thursday I concentrated on the course and the

opposition. I'd ridden at Exeter only once before, and that was two years ago. I didn't remember a great deal about the course other than it was hilly with trees lining the outside of most of the back straight.

The reruns of the three-mile steeplechases showed a downhill stretch when heading into the back straight. There were then four fences more or less in a line with the course going uphill. The third of the four was an open ditch (a normal fence but with a ditch in front of it) and, after the next, the course swung right-handed and went downhill.

There were four fences in the straight and they came in quite quick succession; the first of them was only two furlongs from the finish and was slightly downhill as was the next. At the final fence there was a car park on the other side of the rails and early on the run-in there was a path across the course, seemingly covered with sand or sawdust. I couldn't make out which but it didn't seem to bother the horses. None of them tried to jump it.

Clearly a tricky course which would take more knowing than you could learn from just riding there once. Its hilly nature looked like providing problems of its own because I'd been told never to try and make up ground going uphill – it took far more out of a horse than doing so on the level.

I looked at the betting: Halton Manor was a 10-1 chance and the hot favourite, at 6-4, was Great Gables ridden by the champion amateur Ben Walters. The horse was still technically a novice but he had won his last two races in style and this was his first handicap. Walters was one of three of the ten amateur jockeys in the race to have ridden so many winners that he did not claim an allowance. The other seven, me included, claimed 7lb as we hadn't ridden twenty winners.

I went through the form. Great Gables stood out even though he had gone up quite sharply in the weights, and he looked hard to beat. The next two in the betting had each-way chances but it was hard to envisage any of the others – Halton Manor included – winning the race.

There were other considerations so far as I was concerned. I went through the whole card. Neither Bob Arrows nor Tom Swarter had a runner, and Harry Jones was riding elsewhere. But were the jigger twins the only ones training horses with electric whips? And was I right in assuming that they, or rather their owner George Rickards, were the ones responsible for my assault?

Lastly I studied the weather forecast: dry today but tomorrow morning rain sweeping in from the west. Good. I hoped there would be plenty of it.

12

It was just after 11.00am when we drove into the car park on Friday. After picking up Emma at Tilehurst at 8.30am we'd had a good run. Admittedly almost all of it was on the motorway but we'd covered the 160-odd miles comfortably within the time I'd allowed. There was still an hour and a half before the first and my race wasn't until the third.

Even better, it had been raining since Bristol, not hard but persistently. I put on my cap, riding mac and wellingtons but left my laptop and notes in the car – I knew there would be nobody in the press room this early, and I didn't want to risk anything being pinched. I took my saddle and the bag containing my riding gear with us to the weighing room. The first person we met was the Clerk of the Course. The sometimes-appropriately named Jack Frost was a cheerful middle-aged character, adding to his slightly eccentric image with waterproofs and the sort of sou'wester normally only seen on board a lifeboat in a storm.

I introduced Emma who was wearing a coat rather than a mac, plus a colourful scarf wrapped fashionably over her blonde hair. Jack Frost seemed to be entranced, answering my questions about the going while hardly taking his eyes off Emma.

Next stop the jockeys' room where I spoke briefly to valet Jim Simons, the ex-jockey who I normally used. He pointed me to a peg on the far side, said he had reserved it for me and hung my bag from it.

I took Emma to the restaurant overlooking the course – not that you could see much of it with the rain reducing visibility to little more than fifty yards, ordered her a cup of coffee and set out on my journey round the racecourse.

It was about two miles but I covered much more ground than that. I was particularly interested in the back straight and its four fences going steadily uphill. I walked that bit twice, checking out where the ground had been cut up at recent meetings and where the going was fastest. I had expected to find that I should avoid the inside but it wasn't as straightforward as that. On some parts the best ground was quite some way out from the rails, not so on other sections.

I also made a point of studying the strip that led out of the back straight where the course went downhill. It was the obvious place to kick on. With so little space between each of the last four fences, you would have little time to recover if your horse made even one mistake.

'Hi Rod,' a female voice called out as I ducked under the rails and headed back towards the weighing room. It was Brenda. She grinned broadly from beneath a yellow peaked cap as I walked towards her, a matching jersey under her waterproof navy windcheater. 'This 'll suit Halton,' she said, pointing up at the rain still coming down. "I reckon you could win today.'

'So do I,' I responded, giving her a peck on the cheek and a hug, before falling into stride beside her. She was also making for the weighing room. When we got there, I asked if the doctor had arrived and was pointed to a grey-haired man in silver-framed glasses looking about sixty. He nodded in my direction. I fished my medical card out of my mac pocket and handed it to him. 'Was told to report to you before riding again. This is my first day back.'

He studied the book, smiled and said: 'How's the arm? Hundred per cent?'

When I assured him I was ready to go, and could wait no longer, he smiled again and handed back the book. 'I'll note it in my records,' he said. 'Let's hope it's a winning return.'

Everybody seemed to be boosting my confidence. I retrieved my laptop from the car and went to reserve a spot in the press room. Tom Cameron was already in situ, busily typing away. 'Hi Rod,' he greeted.' You OK again?'

I thanked him for his help at Ludlow.

'You're taking on a tough nut today. They reckon Great Gables is Cheltenham material. By my calculations he's thrown in at the weights.'

Tom Cameron knew what he was talking about. I tried not to look put out. 'Well, maybe, 'I conceded. 'But mine's a good jumper and the ground will help him.'

I glanced at my watch. It was over an hour since I'd left Emma with nothing more to occupy the time than a cup of coffee. I hurried towards the stands. The restaurant looked quite different three-quarters full, and it took me a few seconds to pick out Emma even though she was still at the same table. With her was a man with his back to me. He turned when Emma waved in my direction. It was Ben Walters.

We were only on nodding terms but he stood up and shook me by the hand. 'Hi Rod, good to see you.' His unenthusiastic expression didn't match the words and, muttering something about needing to get changed, he said goodbye to Emma. 'Lovely to meet you and to talk to you.' This time he did sound as if he meant it. Indeed he bent down to kiss her on the cheek. 'Hope we'll see each other again soon,' and left.

'What a nice man,' Emma said, a little too enthusiastically. 'We had a long chat. I gather he's the principal opposition.'

In more ways than one, apparently. I tried to change the subject. 'What about lunch, what would you like?' I picked up the menu and handed it to her.

She studied it. 'What are you going to have?'

'Nothing. Not yet, anyway.' I explained about not wanting to ride with even a half-full stomach in case I had a fall.

'In that case I'll wait too.'

She accompanied me back to the weighing room where she said that, now it had finally stopped raining, she would have a walk round while I got ready. I met up with her as the runners for the first were going down to the start and we watched the race from the stands. Billy Black, still on a roll, got up in the last few strides.

I changed into my riding gear and, with Jim Simons' help, put enough lead into the weight cloth for the trial scales to show the required 10st 11lb. I went back to the press room (Tom Cameron: 'Great Gables is 6-4 on. You've gone out to

12-1') and watched the second race without really taking anything in - my mind was taken up with the next one. Back to the weighing room, stood on the scales and found Paddy O'Reilly waiting to take the saddle. 'Jaysus, this fecking rain. Slowed the traffic no end. I only got here just in time.'

Fifteen minutes later I was in the parade ring listening to his instructions and watching the ten runners circling. Halton Manor looked relaxed and well in himself but Great Gables, I was glad to see, was tossing his head around anxiously. He seemed to know what was coming and it was worrying him.

'Yer man is getting worked up,' said Paddy, grinning cheerfully. 'Now Rod, Halton stays all day but he has fek all acceleration,' the trainer's tone turned serious. 'If he is travelling well enough, don't be afraid to go on quite some way out. But don't try to quicken on the uphill bits. If you do, you'll empty him.'

I nodded. The bell rang for the riders to mount. We walked over to where Brenda had brought the horse to a halt. 'Where's Christopher?' I asked, realising for the first time that the owner wasn't here.

'Sends his apologies,' said Paddy as he legged me into the saddle. 'Some emergency board meeting. Said he'll take time out to watch on TV.' I knotted my reins, and checked my stirrup leathers were the right length, as Brenda led us out towards the course. When she let the horse go, wishing me luck, he broke into a canter and the sudden surge of power beneath my knees filled me with hope.

Halton travelled easily round to the start which was almost immediately after the first fence in the back straight. Several of the runners were already there including the favourite. Ben Walters was walking him round in a circle but well away from the other runners and, I was pleased to see, the horse's neck was in a lather.

I walked Halton over to him and began trotting round in a tight circle, going close to Great Gables each time. 'Fuck off, Hutchinson,' called out Walters. 'You're upsetting my horse.'

'Sorry Ben, didn't catch that.' I did another circuit and was again told to eff off. I steered Halton back towards the others and was delighted to hear Walters calling for the starter's assistant to come and wipe the sweat off his horse's neck.

Three minutes later, girths checked and tightened where necessary, and goggles pulled down, we were called into line and the starter dropped his flag. The early pace was sensible, particularly as we were going uphill, and I settled in fourth well wide of the rails. Out of the corner of my eye I could see that Ben Walters had anchored his horse at the back and was also keeping him to the better ground.

Going past the winning post for the first time the gallop was still quite steady, too steady if I was to have any chance of beating the favourite. I fractionally shortened my reins, gave Halton a kick and he quickened sufficiently to lead. He was jumping well, nothing spectacular but neat and economical at every fence. Going up the back straight he didn't seem to mind the erratic path I directed him to take. I glanced back. Great Gables was still at the back, some ten lengths away and his rider was steering much the same sort of in-and-out passage as I was.

As we turned to swing downhill towards the last four fences, I kicked and went six lengths clear. But, out of the corner of my eye, I could see the favourite making ground and he was travelling ominously easily. My horse continued to jump well, taking the first three of the last four fences with the same neat precision that had characterised his jumping throughout.

I glanced back to see Great Gables now only four lengths behind. And Walters was sitting motionless, oozing confidence with the race seemingly his for the taking. I knew it was now or never - the moment that some of the old-time jockeys called 'all duck or no dinner.' Twenty yards from the final fence, with Great Gables almost literally breathing down my neck, I picked up my whip and gave my horse a crack. Two strides from the fence, I gave him another and shouted 'Hup.'

He soared into the air a stride earlier than he should have done, or would have done had I not thrown caution to the wind and gambled on his jumping. Many horses would have hit the top of the fence and come crashing down. But Halton really reached for it, his forelegs stretched, and somehow he took it cleanly and landed running.

The crash behind me told me that the favourite was not so fortunate. Seeing Halton take off, he had done the same half a stride later and hit the top of the fence hard. He didn't fall but it broke his momentum and knocked some of the stuffing out of him.

But all the way to the line I could hear him getting closer and closer, and Walters shouting at him to find more. Fifty yards out Great Gables' head was at my knee, but Halton Manor had not got this far only to be denied. His ears went back as he dug deep and fought as if his life depended on it. We swept past the post a neck to the good.

'You bastard. I'll get you for that,' Walters shouted at me as we pulled up. I was so thrilled I was unable to stop grinning. I turned my horse and cantered back towards the winner's enclosure with Brenda running towards us in delight.

Paddy was already waiting in the spot reserved for the winner, a broad smile on his face. 'Brilliant,' he enthused. 'Put that arrogant sod Walters in his place. And I was on at 12-1.'

I took the saddle off, weighed in and was promptly grabbed by the Attheraces man who took me off for an interview. He seemed more interested in Brown River's chances at Bangor the next day than today's win but, I soon realised, these questions were merely a warm-up for his main purpose, the attack at Ludlow on Monday. He asked who I thought was responsible, what damage they had done, why they did it and if I was expecting more of the same.

I didn't have anything new to tell him but, knowing how frustrating it is to have your questions stone-walled, I answered as fully as I could. In any case, feeling on top of the world after my win, I wanted to be as helpful as possible. 'Yes,' I added at the end. 'I think I know which bookmaker was behind it but obviously I can't say until I can prove it.'

'Do you intend to find out?'

'Very much so.'

Emma, who had come up halfway through, gave me a hug and a kiss as I stepped down from the interviewer's platform. She came with me to the press room where Tom Cameron, still sitting in front of his laptop, was watching a rerun. 'Well done. But you got a bit lucky. Look,' he added as me and Ben Walters headed into the final fence. 'Great Gables would have won on the bridle if he hadn't made that balls-up.'

It was hard not to disagree. My gamble had paid off but I wasn't going to say anything about it to Tom. I had my own story to write. I told Emma to stay put while I went to get my jacket from the jockeys' room. The riders were just going out for the next. Billy Black broke off to shake me by the hand. Robbie Bolton and Alec Smith also congratulated me. 'That was some trick at the last,' said Smith, grinning broadly. 'I'll need to be careful next time I'm upsides you coming to the final fence.'

I knew it was tongue in cheek – a jockey of Smith's calibre was hardly likely to be taken in like that. Nor would Walters, for that matter, had it not been for his mount's inexperience. For some reason, though, I felt thrilled at what I regarded as a compliment.

Back in the press room Emma was the only one there. 'How about lunch now?' I suggested, expecting her to say she was starving.

'Listen,' she replied. 'I know you've got your article to write. Why don't I just get us some sandwiches, and then you won't be under any pressure?'

I fished in my pocket for a tenner and asked her to also get some tea and cakes, and some for Tom as well.

My phone rang as she was leaving. I thought it must be Brett but it was a number I didn't recognise. 'Rod. Christopher. Well done. That was fantastic.'

In my excitement I'd forgotten all about the owner. I thanked him for the ride and said how well his horse had jumped, and how bravely he had fought on the run-in.

Mayhew talked for a couple of minutes, mainly about the horse, but at the end he said: "Let's hope this is just the first of many winners you ride in my colours.'

The implication was huge. I knew he had some twenty horses and most of them were of a far higher class than Halton Manor. My thoughts fast-forwarded to the Cheltenham Festival in March.

Emma returned with a waitress bearing sandwiches, cakes and tea at the same time as Tom who, sitting down, said: 'Sorry, I forgot. The manager was in earlier. Said she had organised for a security man to patrol between here and the car park until after we've all left.'

'That's great,' I acknowledged, noticing Emma's worried expression. I made sure that I finished my report before the last race. I filed it immediately afterwards, rang Brett to confirm receipt and we were the other side of Bristol before it really got dark.

'What does Ben Walters do for a living?' Emma asked out of the blue.

'Something in his father's property company, I think. They're rolling in it. Why? Have I got a rival for your affections?'

She chuckled. 'I think it's more a case of me having a rival for yours.' She then added, in a quieter and more serious voice: 'Judging by the way you were greeting that girl Brenda. Even Ben remarked on it.'

'Don't be ridiculous.' I reached for her hand and squeezed it. 'It's you I love.' I said it without thinking, the words coming out as if they were the most natural thing in the world.

As the implications slowly dawned on me, I reached for her hand again and gave it another squeeze. After several seconds of silence, she reached for mine on the wheel and gently returned the gesture.

Hardly a word was said by either of us until, passing Swindon, I turned south towards Marlborough. 'There's a pub I've passed going to Paddy's place. It's meant to be a good place to eat.'

The Hare And Hounds did not disappoint. We then went to Reading and almost straight to bed. When we were sitting up, relaxing after love-making, Emma gently stroked my naked chest and said quietly: 'Did you mean what you said in the car?'

I knew immediately what she was referring to. "Of course I did. I'm in love with you.'

She snuggled closer and, giving my left ear a sharp nip with her teeth, whispered: 'And I'm in love with you, my darling.'

Bloody Hell. Among Brown River's eleven opponents in the Wrexham District Handicap Chase was Grey Somali, and Bob Arrows had two other runners during the afternoon. All three were to be ridden by Harry Jones who was also down to ride one for Tom Swarter in the first.

I was parked in a layby on the Oxford bypass eating my breakfast - muesli, sugar and milk hastily poured into a thermos before taking Emma to Tilehurst at 7.30am – and studying the Bangor card in the *Racing Post*, acutely conscious that I hadn't done my homework.

Was one of the horses an electric whip job? Was it Grey Somali again? I cursed. I really should have stuck to my original intention of spending at least an hour going through the runners yesterday evening. Instead I'd given into temptations of the flesh as soon as we got back to the flat. I grabbed the tinfoil containing my toast off the back seat, started the engine and pulled out into the A34 to head for the motorways around Birmingham.

Fortunately the traffic was quick, even after I left the M54 shortly before Shifnal to make for the Whitchurch bypass, and I pulled into the racecourse car park just after 11.00am. I had almost an hour and a half before the first and my race wasn't until 2.15pm. After leaving my bag with Jim Simons in the jockeys' room, I grabbed my binoculars and in wellingtons walked over to what passed for a grandstand at Bangor. The long grass-covered mound gave a good view of the course, particularly as the weather was clear but cold, with a weak wintery sun trying to break through. I'd been to Bangor twice before but this was the first time I'd ridden here.

The two and a half mile start was at the top end of a triangle, and the furthest part from the mound. I walked past the winning post and past three fences before I got to that point. I was surprised to see how testing the ground had become – Friday's rain had obviously come here too, and there must have been more of it than at Exeter. But Brown River acted in any going except firm. The fences were nice and wide although the course became alarmingly narrow in places. Presumably they kept moving the rails to stop the inside becoming poached.

Walking down the second side of the triangle, past what would be the first four fences in my race, I could see what looked like a river – the Dee I presumed – only a field away with sheep between it and the racecourse. The course became very narrow again shortly before the straight where there were two more fences leading to the winning post. At that point in the race we would be going round again.

I didn't walk it a second time – I felt I didn't need to, and I was getting hungry. I went to the snack bar and bought a sandwich. Although I always tried not eat before race-riding, I felt I needed to keep my strength up. Getting my laptop out of the car, I found I was parked next to Tom Cameron who was sitting behind the wheel studying a road map.

'Hi Rod,' he wound down the window. 'Going to win again? Horse's got a good chance, I reckon.' I changed my footwear and we walked together to the press room where a man in his sixties, a brown overcoat and a flat cap, was already in residence in front of the TV. He stood up, shook hands and said he was here for the Wrexham Leader.

I studied Tom Swarter's runner in the parade ring before the first. The chestnut ambled round looking normal enough, no sweating or other sign of nerves, even when the trainer legged Harry Jones into the saddle. He ran much the same way, mid-division for most of the two mile journey, quickening a bit between the last two hurdles. But there was no sudden surge and he finished an unexciting fifth.

Bob Arrows' runner in the next, also a maiden hurdle, was almost a carbon copy except that he made up some ground before the second last and might have finished third but for weakening on the run-in.

Were they waiting for Grey Somali?

I went to the jockeys' room to change and was stopped in the weighing room by a thin-looking red-haired man in his early thirties, in waterproof jacket and jeans. 'Hi Mr 'Utchinson.' I wondered what he wanted. 'John Smithers, deputy travelling head lad.'

I hadn't seen him before and said so. 'Only been with the stable a month and we're short-handed today. The guv'nor's gone to Lingfield. Just me and the horse came up in the Lambourn Transport box.'

'Where's Manch?' I was suspicious. Trevor, for all his off-handedness and other faults, always made sure he had a full complement of staff when he had runners.

'He's not with us anymore. That's partly why we're short-handed.'

'What happened? How come he left?' Manch Wilkinson was loyal and dedicated to the core.

'Had a row with the boss and walked out yesterday.' John Smithers shrugged his shoulders. 'Don't know the details.'

Smithers said he would come back immediately after the next to collect my saddle. I changed, got Jim Simons to check the trial scales before going to the clerk of the scales to weigh out. Brown River's 10st 7lb, after deduction of my 7lb claim, was no problem. Being quite thin, I could comfortably ride at 9st 10lb. But I was worried. Manch leaving? What the hell was going on? And was Brown River going to be affected?

I put on my coat and walked over to the line of bookmakers. Grey Somali was favourite at 11-4 and Brown River next on 7-2. Much as I expected. Nothing in the market to suggest anything fishy. Not yet.

When I walked into the parade ring with the other riders Grey Somali was the one that took my eye. He had his head up, ears pricked, as he looked round at the crowd and beyond them to the racecourse. His coat was glistening and his whole being suggested a horse ready to race. Brown River, with John Smithers leading him, also looked in the picture of health. When the bell went, the horses were halted and I walked over to mine. As he gave me a leg up into the saddle, Smithers said: 'The guv'nor said to tell you the horse couldn't be better. Ride him handy and go on before the second last. You should win, he said.'

Why hadn't he said anything about Grey Somali? I knotted my reins, put my weight on one side of the saddle and then the other to check I had my stirrups the right length, and broke into a canter the minute we got out onto the course. Brown River went down ears pricked, moving easily as we passed the three fences on the way to the start. As we circled, I tightened my girths. The horse came to a halt and I could feel him emptying his bladder. He seemed to have a lot to empty. I looked again at Grey Somali. Harry Jones called out as he passed: 'Should be your turn this time Rod – five pound turnaround in the weights.'

The starter called us into line and we were off. I found myself on the heels of Grey Somali who was well placed in fourth. Nobody made even a semblance of a mistake at the first, nor at the next three fences. The pace was quite good considering the ground. At least it looked like being a true run race and that should favour the better fancied runners.

As we turned into the straight Brown River seemed to roll to his right. He did at again after jumping the next fence, and I thought I could detect him struggling to get his breath. Not continuously, just twice. But by the time we passed the winning post with a circuit to run he was labouring. And we were falling back in the field. I urged him to pick up. He didn't respond. I gave him a slap with the whip, his ears went back and he went even slower. What the hell was wrong?

I glanced down – but he didn't seem to be lame. We were now last and, as we neared the first of the four fences heading out towards the starting point, he was almost twenty lengths behind the second last horse. He could barely get over the fence and, as he struggled to stay on his feet on the landing side, I pulled him up and got off.

I checked him out as best I could. Still nothing obvious. But something was wrong, very wrong. I pulled the reins over his head and, as I began the walk back to the unsaddling area, it hit me. The Grey Somali people knew that it was me who had seen their electric whip modus operandi, and they wanted their revenge. What better way than to stop my horse, particularly when I was riding him. And George Rickards? Well, the *weRthebestbets.com* operator had revealed his true colours at Ludlow only five days earlier.

By the time I reached an anxious John Smithers I was seething. 'What happened?' he wanted to know. Before I could answer, the grey-haired tweed-suited man standing beside him said to me: 'Bring him to the veterinary box, I'll check him out and take samples.'

'John 'll take him,' I said, handing the reins to Smithers. 'I'm going to see the stewards.'

I strode angrily through the weighing room, knocked on the door marked 'Stewards Only' and walked straight in.

'Please wait outside until you are called, Mr Hutchinson.' Just my luck to have Lawrence Matthews on duty.

'No. Wait,' intervened one of the men sitting at the long table facing the big TV. The large burly figure in a check suit promptly confirmed my impression that this was the chairman of the acting stewards by saying: 'We need Mr er ...' he ran a stubby finger down the racecard open in front of him ... 'Here we are ... Hutchinson to explain why he pulled his horse up.'

'Sir, he was in trouble by the time we got to the straight first time round. He seemed to roll to the right and he became short of breath.'

'What do you think was wrong?'

I looked down the row of faces at the table, and then at a glaring Lawrence Matthews. 'I don't think. I know. He was got at.'

There was a stunned silence, eventually broken by Matthews. 'That will be for the veterinary officer, and the laboratory, to decide. We have already asked the course vet to examine the horse and take samples for analysis.' Looking questioningly at the chairman, he continued. 'I think that will be all for now, Mr Hutchinson.'

His insistence on placing the emphasis on the word mister did nothing to mollify my anger and, nodding at the chairman, I walked out, grabbed my coat from the almost-deserted jockeys' room – most of the riders were in the parade ring for the next race- and headed for the veterinary box. The horse, the vet and Smithers were still there.

'No trouble with the urine sample,' said the vet cheerfully. 'He pissed for Wales. We've done the blood too and I've checked his heart. Nothing wrong there and he's not lame either.'

As I walked back towards the press room, thinking about what the vet said, something registered. Surely not, though?

If what I thought might have happened had in fact done so, it would – in my eyes at least – be just about the biggest betrayal since Judas Iscariot.

'Something wrong with the horse?' asked Tom Cameron, lifting his head from his laptop as I resumed my seat.

'The vet says not – not physically anyway.'

'But you think differently?'

I knew Cameron was fishing. I wanted to tell him – and I owed him for Ludlow - but I also had a story to write. At the same time, I was bursting to tell someone. 'He was lurching to the right coming into the straight. And, after the next two fences, he was exhausted. Been working well at home - so I'm told anyway.'

I realised I'd said too much when I saw him scribbling away in his notepad. And, I saw, he could do shorthand. I stood up, muttering something about needing to get changed, and left before he could quiz me any further.

Doing my report an hour or so later though, I didn't mince words and was rewarded with a 'Pity – but a great story' comment from Brett.

I left soon after the last and I was only about ten miles short of the M54 by the time the automatic headlights came on. But it was on the Oxford bypass that the phone rang. 'Emma' flashed onto the screen.

I cheered up immediately. 'Hi. How's things?'

She didn't reply. I thought the connection had broken until I heard a sobbing noise. After about ten seconds it came again.

'Emma. Are you alright?'

No answer, just another sob. 'Rob,' she said eventually. I could hear her crying. 'Those men. They attacked me.'

'God, Emma. Are you alright?'

'No.' The sobbing came again. 'They were waiting for me when I got out of the car at my flat.' I could sense her trying to fight back the tears. 'They cut my throat with a knife, like they did to you. Said 'Your boyfriend wouldn't listen. Maybe he will listen to you.' More tears and sobs. 'Rod, I'm so frightened.'

'Emma, please listen to me. Lock yourself into the flat. Whatever you do, don't open the door. I will be with you in just under an hour. OK?'

'OK. But Rod, please come as quick as you can. I'm frightened.' She sobbed again, and the line went dead.

13

I moved up a gear, mentally as well as with the BMW, threw caution to the wind and raced to Tilehurst as fast as I dared. I roared into the grounds of the big house and pulled up spraying gravel in all directions. There were lights on in all three storeys as well as outside the front door. It opened as I reached it.

'Oh Emma. I'm so sorry.' I reached for her to take her in my arms.

'No.' She pulled away, turned and headed quickly up the first flight of stairs. Clearly she was even more upset than I thought.

Once inside the flat I moved to embrace her again. 'No Rod. Don't. Sit down. I need to talk to you.'

I sat on the sofa on which we had so passionately embraced, expecting more of the same once she had spoken what was on her mind.

But she didn't join me. Instead she took the armchair opposite. I could see traces of dried blood on both sides of her neck.

'Rodney Hutchinson, you are obsessed. With your racing – and obsessed with your writing,' she began. Her tone was serious, her face grim-set. 'You don't care what damage you cause. You don't care what danger you put yourself in. And you don't care what danger you put other people in. Even people close to you.'

There was barely a pause as she delivered what was clearly a prepared speech - and prepared in anger.

I could see the tears welling up in her eyes. I wanted, more than anything, to hold her tight and comfort her. I moved to get to my feet.

'No. Don't.' The cry was determined, and it was delivered with fury. I sat down again, and the assault continued. 'You are dangerous to know. You are bad news – and I want you out of my life.'

This time it was Emma who got to her feet. "Now, please go. And, please, don't ever try to contact me again. You and I are finished.'

I stood up. If only I could get my arms around her I was sure she would melt into a loving embrace, despite the furious glare she was directing at me.

I turned as I reached the door. 'Emma, please.'

'No!' Her voice was raised almost to screaming pitch. I could hear doors opening as her yell brought out other residents.

I turned and, ignoring the stares of the grey-haired lady

next door and the ex-military looking man on the other side, headed down the stairs. My mind was in turmoil as I reached the car, fumbled for the ignition and drove slowly through the big wrought-iron gates.

It wasn't all that far from Tilehurst to Kennet Walk. Just as well because I hardly saw the other traffic or noticed which way I was going. By some miracle all the lights were on green. Had they not been, I might well have gone straight across. I was on autopilot, noticing almost nothing as my mind kept running through Emma's diatribe and the hatred with which it was delivered.

Once inside the flat, with a large brandy in one hand and the remote controlling the Bangor-on-Dee reruns in the other, I was no better. The all-consuming replay in mind wouldn't switch off. No sooner did I think I was managing to put it behind me than it came back clearer than ever. Every word, every inflection, every nuance. But above all else the cold fury.

I hardly saw Brown River's race. He was out of the picture for most of it and Emma still filled my mind, even to the exclusion of the scrambled egg supper I made and ate without thinking or tasting.

In the bath I saw that much of the bruising on my stomach was still there but, thank God, fading fast. I needed to find some plusses on what, I was convinced, had been one of the worst days of my life. Brown River's defeat, and the way he ran, was bad enough but to lose Emma was even worse. I'd been jilted before – too many times – but not by a girl that I truly loved. Indeed, I now realised, I had never before been properly in love.

In the middle of a night in which I hardly slept I considered going back to life as a solicitor and trying to win her back that way. But could I really sacrifice the excitement of the racecourse, the fascination of its characters, the adrenalin rush and thrill of race-riding, of trying to win and the satisfaction of getting a good story for a life of conveyancing, local court appearances and neighbours' arguments day after day, week after week? The prospect appalled me.

I was still stunned, sitting at the kitchen table in pyjamas and dressing gown, sipping a cup of tea, when the doorbell rang shortly after 8.00am. My heart rose. Maybe it was Emma coming to make it up. As I pulled back the yale, the door burst open and a big, powerful man grabbed me by the throat. He slammed my head so hard against the wall that I cried out.

The thugs were back. Stupid bastard - I should have been more careful before responding to the ring as if it was the old lady in the next flat wanting to borrow a bowl of sugar. Fear brought the pain in my stomach flooding back. I wasn't sure I could survive a second bout of pile-driving from a *weRthebestbets.com* punishment-beater.

'You miserable little bugger,' the big man began, his huge right hand still grasping my neck. He slammed my head against the wall a second time. The impact jolted through my brain like the shock in an American-style electric chair. Again I cried out in agony.

'Don't you ever go near my daughter again.' So this was the vet. 'If you do, I'll make sure you never write another word ever again. Understand?' His grip on my neck tightened to such an extent that I couldn't get my breath, let alone nod.

'Do you understand, you horrible fucking piece of shit?' The big, powerful hand around my neck began to shake my head from side to side. I cried out - and was rewarded with a violent punch in the gut. It was as if all the life had been slammed out of me. And the pain was indescribable.

The vice-like grip was relaxed as I collapsed to the floor, clutching my stomach in agony.

'I'm waiting for an answer.' The big brown shoe inches from my face was pulled back as if to deliver a kick. 'No, please.' I croaked. 'I won't have anything more to do with Emma. I promise.'

Her father reached down, grabbed me by the dressing gown front and slammed me against the wall yet again. 'If you do, I'll kill you,' he shouted in my face from a distance of three inches. I fell back down again as he pulled open the door and slammed it behind him.

As I lay on the floor, too shocked and too hurt to move, I vaguely heard my phone ringing. Gritting my teeth in pain, I managed to crawl back to the kitchen. I pulled myself up to the height of the table and slumped onto a chair. The best part of ten minutes elapsed before I could move sufficiently to put the kettle back on. I was tempted to put brandy in the tea. But I had things to sort out. I couldn't afford to give in to the pain this time.

Again the phone rang. Again I couldn't get there. But supposing it was Emma? The possibility, and the hope, made me get up and fetch it from the bedroom.

Two missed calls, both from the same number. It wasn't Emma. As the hope disappeared, the pain reasserted itself in earnest. I was doubled up trying to somehow lessen the excruciating torture in my middle as I pressed the call button.

'Hello. Is that you Rod?' The voice was vaguely familiar. 'It's Manch.'

'Oh Manch,' I managed. 'How's things?'

'Terrible.' Somebody else having a bad day. 'About Brown River yesterday. Do you know what happened?'

'Yes, well I think I do. Somebody got at him.'

'No,' answered Manch. 'At least not in the way you think.'

'Oh.' Finally something that took my mind off my battered stomach.

'He had no water from Thursday night until shortly before the race.'

'Fucking hell. How come?' So it was the ultimate betrayal. Now I knew why Brown River had run like that. The old adage that you can lead a horse to water but you can't make it drink went by the board if the horse in question had been deprived of liquid for some time, particularly if - like Brown River - the animal was fed on concentrates. He would have drunk buckets. With gallons of water swilling round in his stomach, he wouldn't have been able to travel at racing pace for long.

'The guv'nor told me on Thursday evening to take the water bucket out of his box, and give him no more until an hour before the race on Saturday. I argued with him. That's why I got the sack. I wanted to ring you yesterday to warn you. But the race was over by the time I managed to get the number out of *sports-all.com*.'

'Shit.' So that was why he peed so much at the start - and I recalled the vet's words: 'He pissed for Wales.'

'What about job-wise now. What will you do?'

'Dunno. Got a month's money to tide me over while I look.'

My mind fast-forwarded to the rest of the day. 'I've an idea. Might work, might not. But I'll ring you this evening - either way.'

It was just after 10.30am when I drove between the two stone pillars and came to a halt in front of the small white house. Paddy O'Reilly emerged from the door at the side, usual brown windcheater and jeans but slippers instead of riding boots, curiosity written all over his face.

'Hi Rod,' he said enquiringly. 'Didn't expect to see you today.'

He invited me inside when I said I needed to talk and, as I began, he pointed me to one of the armchairs and said he would be back in a couple of minutes. But I followed him through into the kitchen and helped myself to one of the chairs around the table while Paddy put the kettle on, brought out a plate of biscuits and a jug of milk.

'Mary's gone to church,' he said as he filled the teapot, and gave it a stir before pouring into two mugs. He pushed one, and the biscuit plate, in my direction. 'Help yourself to sugar.'

I explained what had happened at Bangor yesterday, my suspicions at the time and Manch's phone call this morning. I made no mention of my vicious visitor and the punch in the stomach. It was the horses I need to talk about.

'Jaysus. Yer man Trevor seems to have quite an agenda,' he said as I got near the end. 'Tought that when Ezekiel won at Ludlow on Monday with a fecking fortune on him. He wants you out of t'way, alright.'

'But why Paddy? And why doesn't he just say so?'

'Dunno about that last bit. But reckon it's all to do with that brother of his, Jimmy. He's going into the Flat in a big way, buying all them expensive yearlings. More money in Flat racing. Yer don't need to be fecking Einstein to realise Trevor needs the boxes for the Flat horses. So the jumpers have to go.'

'Yes,' I said slowly, thinking hard and helping myself to another biscuit. Breakfast had been almost non-existent after that punch in the gut.

'Jimmy's big into betting too. Ezekiel was his money, you can be sure of that – and the last thing he needs is a journalist in the stable. He'd be worried you might blow the gaffe.'

Now it was making sense. Although I still couldn't understand why Trevor hadn't simply told me that the yard was closing down its jump racing, and that I needed to find another trainer.

I swallowed the rest of my tea. 'Paddy, the other reason I came to talk to you today was to ask you if you would take Brown River and Ezekiel.'

'That 'd be grand.' He didn't hesitate. 'Two decent horses. I have to speak to Chris before taking on any new owner. That's the arrangement. But I can tell you now he won't object. Quite the opposite. He thinks a lot of you.'

Paddy stood up. 'I'll give you next year's terms.' He disappeared into the sitting room and came back with a sheet of paper. I was pleased to see that the training fees were less than Trevor's current ones, let alone next year's eight per cent increase.

'When are you planning to transfer the horses?'

'Ideally tomorrow. I'm going there now.'

'Fine,' he grinned. 'At least it will be when I get a couple more lads. I've got a further three horses coming on Tuesday.'

I told him about Manch and how good he had been with my two. Paddy seemed enthusiastic. 'That's grand. Tell him to give me a ring as soon as possible.'

I stood up, and said I would like to give Halton a carrot before leaving for Lambourn.

'Oh, I almost forgot,' said Paddy as he got to his feet and reached for his cap. 'You OK for Cheltenham on Saturday?'

'Sure.' I was puzzled. Surely he couldn't mean it?

'We're running Mr Bombastic in the three-mile amateur chase. Want him to get to know the course before the National Hunt Chase.'

I was lost for words. I'd never ridden at Cheltenham and now it looked as if I could be in action there at the hallowed National Hunt Festival when each of the four day's racing attracted over 50,000 people.

'He won't be trying too hard, though Rod.' Paddy grinned, showing two gaps in his teeth. 'He's a horse we think a lot of. Won both his point-to-point starts in Ireland and cost a fecking fortune. Christopher brought in a couple of pals to share the cost. He ran fourth on his first start here at Warwick and was then second at Huntingdon. This 'll be a tougher race altogether but the experience of the course is what it's all about.'

We walked together to the far end of the yard, my mind envisaging that famous climb after the last fence to the winning post, while Paddy greeted by name each face that stuck it's head out of it's box. The yard was empty of people. Halton Manor was watching us coming, he grabbed the carrot and crunched it between his yellowing teeth with evident satisfaction. I gave him a grateful pat and realised I should have brought a second carrot when he began determinedly nuzzling my jersey.

'Can you come and ride on Wednesday? We'll give Mr Bombastic a canter and put him over a couple of fences.'

Still on a Cheltenham cloud nine, I readily agreed.

I pulled into the car park in front of the Hare And Hounds, trying not to think about Emma and our meal here on Friday evening, and rang Manch. I told him my two horses were moving to Paddy O'Reilly on Monday, that Paddy was looking for staff and was expecting his call.

Going on to Lambourn, I rehearsed what I was going to say to Trevor. What worried me more, though, was Sarah. How would she react to my decision? Would she see it as disloyalty, if not downright treachery? I didn't want to fall out with her. But I couldn't see any way of avoiding that.

The yard was empty. Sunday was a day off for most stable staff. Carrots in pocket, I walked over to where Ezekiel and Brown River were stabled as horses looked over stable doors, curious about the appearance of someone on such a quiet day.

I gave each of mine a carrot and a pat. 'Morning Mr 'Utchinson.' A lad I just about recognised came up and joined me in front of Brown River's box. 'Seems OK this morning. Pity about yesterday.'

'Where's Trevor?'

'In the house.' He fished his phone out of his pocket and dialled. 'Told me to ring if any of the owners came.' He spoke briefly into the phone. I just about heard my name, and the phone went back into the pocket of his jeans. 'Says he will be out in two minutes.'

It was more like four when Trevor appeared in his usual Sunday corduroys but with a green jersey this time. 'Brown River was fine this morning,' he said. 'Still don't know what went wrong at Bangor. We'll put him on the easy list for a few days, just to be on the safe side.'

'Trevor.' I plucked up courage. 'I'm taking the horses away. Please have my bill emailed to me as soon as the secretaries come in tomorrow. I'll pay it straightaway and send transport, hopefully before lunch.'

Raised eyebrows were just about his only response. 'As you wish. Where are they going?'

I told him. 'Hmm. Good trainer. Horses doing well at the moment.' He turned on his heel and headed back to the house.

I gave both horses a second carrot and looked round for the lad. But there was no sign. I walked briskly back to the car and drove off, thankful that Sarah hadn't been involved.

But as I got onto the M4 something struck me. Trevor hadn't asked why I was taking the horses away.

It was mid-morning when George Goodbody's name came up on my phone. By that time the transport had been arranged for noon, and Trevor's bill had been received and paid. I was pleasantly surprised to find that it made no mention of the calendar month's notice that I'd signed up to when I first became an owner with the stable. Indeed the fees only went up to Sunday evening. Maybe Paddy was right - Trevor simply wanted me out of the stable.

'You still trying to find out who's behind *weRthebestbets. com*?' Goodbody asked.

'I think I know actually. It's a man called George Rickards.'

'No. Not according to my informant, and he's never been wrong yet.'

'Oh.' I knew I sounded sceptical. I was.

'The ultimate owner, behind all the Cayman Island companies, is a former investment banker. He lives in Jersey and his name is Michael Henderson. I've got his mobile number if it's of any use.'

'Yes please.'

I wrote it down carefully. 'Who's your informant?'

'Same man but I can't give you his name or his number. That's the condition he insists on. He's a computer expert. Reckons he can get into just about anywhere except the Bank Of England and Fort Knox.' George laughed at what was obviously intended as a joke.

'But he's a gambler. He's won over a hundred grand on your tips in the last few days and he rang this morning to say I must give you the info you were looking for.'

My tips? I seldom did tipping pieces for the website. Maybe he was getting me mixed up with The Major. I said so to George.

'No, he doesn't do anything conventional like that. He's

adamant that the whole thing is fixed, and the way to make money out of it is to do the opposite whenever you get any inside information. He backed Ezekiel because you told me he was only being got ready for your return and he laid Brown River on Saturday because you said he could well win.'

I laughed. Surely he was having me on?

'And Rod. He asks when you will be riding next and what you think of your chances.'

'Probably won't be for a while because both mine have been moved to a new stable this morning.' The last thing I needed was a wholesale gamble on Mr Bombastic. Paddy and Christopher Mayhew – not to mention Brett and my readers - would find themselves thinking I was tied in with a betting syndicate, and as corrupt as a bent copper.

Instead I asked George to thank his contact and say I would be in touch.

I put the phone down as mystified as a child watching a conjuror pull a rabbit out of a hat. If the computer expert was right maybe George Rickards was a pseudonym for Michael Henderson, or vice-versa. Or maybe Goodbody and his informant had been fed false information to lead me into a trap.

I deliberated for the best part of an hour. I decided to ring the number, but first I typed out what I was going to say and printed it off.

I switched on the tape recorder and dialled. 'Henderson,' said a voice at the other end. No accent as such.

I gave my name and said I was writing an article about the success of *weRthebestbets.com*. I'd long since learned that people tend to be suspicious of journalists and, if you want to get an interview, it helps to give the impression that you are going to give them a positive write-up and that you are not going to knock them. I said that I would like to come and see him to get some background information.

I fully expected him to say no and cut the conversation short, if not actually end the call immediately.

'Ah. I'm glad you called Rod because I was intending to ring you this week. When do you want to come?'

To say I was surprised would be like a cat telling the mouse he'd caught that he only wanted to wish it a pleasant day. I mentally ran through the next few days. Wednesday was obviously out.

'How about tomorrow or Thursday?'

'Tomorrow would be better. The new Jersey Air service has a plane leaving Gatwick at nine in the morning. It will be here at ten and I'll have a driver waiting for you in the arrivals hall.'

As I ended the call I wondered if I wasn't being dangerously gullible. Michael Henderson sounded genuine enough, and there wasn't one iota of threat in either what he said or the way he said it. But the Ludlow beating was fresh in my mind, my stomach was still bruised – particularly with Emma's father making it worse - and I hadn't forgotten the warning either. The *weRthebestbets.com* organisation was ruthless in the extreme.

I logged into the Jersey Air site, found the flight and booked a seat as well as the return on the only other AJ plane to Gatwick that day, at 4.00pm.

I just hoped I would be on it.

14

We were only a couple of miles from the French coast when the clouds cleared. With the hazy winter sun shining down, I could just make out what I presumed to be Alderney, and then the captain announced that we were beginning our descent. There were only twenty passengers on the small plane and, judging by their clothes, most were business people.

I'd never been to any of the Channel Islands and I was fascinated as we flew in over the northern part of the island. The small airport seemed to be on the western side and quite some way from St Helier. I had no luggage so went straight through customs to the arrivals hall, and found a driver holding up a board with 'Mr Hutchinson' written on it.

He was a big, burly man of around forty and, disturbingly, he had no uniform or cap to say what company he worked for. Was I walking into the lion's den? I cursed myself for not having told anyone where I was going. I hadn't even left a note in my flat to be opened if I didn't return. Belinda would surely come looking if she hadn't heard from me in a fortnight or so. And Brett would be playing hell.

The driver opened the door of a black Mercedes that reminded me of a funeral car. As we set off I asked the driver if he took many people to see Mr Henderson. 'Not that many,' he replied, his French accent making me concentrate to understand what he was saying. 'Maybe a dozen or so this year.'

'And do you take them all back to the airport?'

There was an ominously long pause. 'Maybe half of them. Not more.'

'So what happened to the other half?'

The driver gave a Gallic shrug of the shoulders as the road turned to reveal a magnificent beach that seemed to stretch from the top to the bottom of the western end of the island. There was even an old-fashioned lighthouse at one end - but all I could think of was a lead-lined coffin and burial at sea. Nobody would ever find the bodies out there.

We turned off the main road, up a narrow lane with very few houses on it. After about two hundred yards we came to a large white two-storey set well back from the road. The driver went slowly up the gravel drive and stopped outside what was clearly the front door. 'Voila,' he announced but almost in a stage whisper.

I thanked him, got out and rang the bell as he drove off. The door opened almost immediately and I was greeted by name by a middle-aged woman in a smart navy suit and white blouse.

'Did you have a good flight?' she asked as she led the way up the wide staircase and ushered me into a large drawing room looking out to sea. 'Mr Henderson is on the phone in his office but he won't be long. He knows you're here. Would you like tea or coffee?'

I went over to the window and looked in the direction of the lighthouse. The beach was deserted. If I disappeared here nobody would ever know.

'Sorry to keep you waiting, Rod.' A tall thin man, about 6' 2" I guessed, breezed in, carrying a sheaf of papers which he put down on the desk in the far corner. I surreptitiously studied him as I memorised his appearance for my article. He was about sixty and his expensive-looking pale yellow jersey, striped shirt and tie, was incongruously matched – or rather unmatched - by a pair of check trousers of the type more normally associated with American golfers.

He glanced down at my notes and tape recorder on the small table in front of me. 'Good,' he said. 'Glad to see you are properly prepared.'

He looked up as the smartly-dressed lady appeared with a tray of coffee, cups, milk and sugar. 'You've met my secretary, Jennifer.' We nodded at each other as she put them down on the table next to my notes. 'Hold my calls for the next hour,' she was instructed.

'Help yourself,' he pointed to the coffee. 'No, not for me. I've had my mine.'

As I poured, he continued: 'I see you have plenty of questions. But let me first tell you who I am, how and why I set up *weRthebestbets.com* and, most importantly, where we are going from here.'

I switched on the tape recorder, and put it down on the table between us, as Michael Henderson related his story. He had been an investment banker all his working life and moved to Jersey to join a St Helier firm twenty years ago. He had long had an interest in racing – 'not so much the horses and jockeys but the bookmaking side' – and, when Covid-19 brought new investment business almost to a halt with most of the bank's workers staying at home, he decided to do something about it.

'As you know, bookmakers price up the horses so that they will make around 16% on turnover. Of course that's the theory. Sometimes they make more, sometimes less – they are gamblers too. But the odds are very much against the punter.' Henderson's tone was businesslike in the extreme.

'Of course bookmakers have overheads – wages, travelling to racemeetings, rents if they operate from a betting shop. But supposing you have no overheads? I won't say it's a licence to print money but, by God, you've got a really profitable business.' His voice raised as he said this, and his mounting enthusiasm was like that of a football commentator describing a hotshot centre-forward about to score a goal.

'When Covid became a matter of life and death, people started doing everything on line. So I thought why not do it for betting too. I deliberately went slowly to start with. I didn't want to run before I knew how to walk and how easily, or otherwise, it would be for me to trip up.'

He explained how, despite his caution, the business had expanded far faster than he had expected, leading to him recruiting two of his investment protegees. Both were financial whiz kids who took to the betting business as if they had been born for nothing else. It was they who launched the advertising campaigns and they who were now pushing for the operation to go public through a placing of shares. 'They were impressed with your previous article about us and they suggested I talk to you.' He steepled his hands in front of his chest. 'We are now actively looking for publicity.'

'But why the secrecy up to now?' I wasn't going to simply swallow the verbal pills I'd been given. 'Nobody knows where you are based, or even who runs the business. And why is your ownership hidden behind a succession of Cayman Island companies?' I leaned forward to make sure the tape recorder was still working.

Henderson smiled. 'You think it's suspicious?' He chuckled. 'It's more the fear of failure. You see, in the banking world you steadily build a reputation for success. It's what convinces banks to lend money and rich men to invest. One flop can put you back years. I thought I could make an online betting firm work but I didn't know for sure. Don't forget, I had no experience whatsoever. I could just as easily have been wrong and failure would blight my name for the rest of my life.'

'Hmm.' I wasn't going to let him get away with that either. 'So who is George Rickards?'

'Who?'

'George Rickards. Don't tell me you don't know who I'm talking about?'

'Sorry Rod. But I know nobody of that name. You think I should?'

I explained that, according to racecourse sources, *weRthebestbets.com* was owned by George Rickards who has some twenty horses with Bob Arrows and Tom Swarter.

'Is George Rickards a pseudonym?'

The investment banker laughed. 'If he is, it's not for Michael Henderson.'

I wasn't convinced. Referring to my notes I changed tack. 'The regular bookmakers I've spoken to say that you give trainers over the odds, and sometimes their money back, when horses go wrong in return for information.'

'Goodness. Would you believe me if I say I have never spoken to a single trainer since I started this operation, indeed not since before Covid?'

This time I was convinced, or nearly so. But, feeling like a gambler with his last throw of the dice, I said: 'Are you saying that it wasn't you who had me beaten up at Ludlow last week?'

'Rod, for God's sake. Do I look like a man who would do that? I thought, reading your columns, you were a man of judgement. But you are coming up with a succession of accusations, each one more preposterous than the last.'

Now I did believe him. I apologised. I should have realised from the moment I met him that I was way out with my assumptions.

Michael Henderson was not best pleased. He stood up. 'Unless you've got any more questions, I have a meeting to go to and I must leave shortly.'

Perhaps realising that he needed the article to read well, he added in a far more conciliatory tone: 'Sorry Rod. Just that I got a bit hot under the collar. I would never do anything like that. And I do understand that you have to ask your questions, if only to prove that racecourse talk is just that – talk.

'Anyway,' he continued, much more affably, 'I owe *sports-all.com* a lot – or at least your man The Major a lot.'

'Because his tips are so good, you mean?' I got to my feet, switched off the tape recorder and picked it up together with my notes.

'Well, obviously. Partly that anyway. But we get his tips emailed to us every morning before they appear on your website.'

I couldn't believe what I was hearing. 'Do you mean he sends them to you?'

'No, not him personally. I'm pretty sure of that. But you know they appear on your website at 9.30am each day together with his article?'

I did. Brett deliberately made sure that they appeared exactly at 9.30am. It was one of his ways of capturing readership.

'We get our email – just the tips, not the article – at around 9.20am. It doesn't come from him but from a post restante server which, for a fee, hides the identity of the sender. I tried to find out but all I could come up with was a second post restante server, and then a third one.'

A bit like those *weRthebestbets.com* shareholdings, I thought. But I felt it prudent not to say so.

'But what I did find out is that we are not the only ones getting this email. Nor the first either.'

I listened, enthralled and horrified. We were both still standing, and I reached for the tape recorder. 'No,' said Henderson, putting out a restraining hand. 'This must be off the record.'

'For weeks I printed off the prices offered by all the main bookmakers on every race each day at 9.00am, again when we received our email and once more just before 9.30am. The first moves always came with Hedgers. Within ten minutes they cut the prices of what proved to be The Major's tips. Other firms followed suit before 9.30am. Possibly because they saw Hedgers' prices change, or because Hedgers had backed the tipped horses with them.'

'Christ Almighty.' I was stunned. The obvious conclusion hit me even more forcibly than the thug in the Ludlow car park.

Further deliberation was cut short by Jennifer putting her head round the door. 'Sorry Michael. But you do know your St Helier appointment is in five minutes.'

Michael Henderson looked at his watch and swore. 'Tell them I'm leaving now and I should be with them in about twenty minutes. Are you still OK to take Rod here back to the airport?'

He shook me by the hand, thanked me for coming and apologised for having to dash off. 'Give me a ring if you need anything else,' he said as he disappeared through the door.

'Just give me five minutes to make that call and we'll go too,' said Jennifer as she exited only seconds later.

The journey to the airport in Jennifer's white Volkswagen didn't take long but long enough for her to tell me that she had been working for Michael Henderson for nearly three years, how his wife was one of the first on Jersey to die of Covid and that his main hobby was golf.

I spent the two and half hours before my flight eating a leisurely airport lunch and pondering the implications of what I'd been told. Clearly Henderson was not the ruthless thug that I'd supposed. But, in that case, who was George Rickards? And what betting operation did he run? Was he involved in Hedgers?

And what was Charles's link to Hedgers? Presumably he was paid by the big bookmaker for supplying his tips twenty minutes before the website readers had a chance to act on them? It was hard to square this blatant act of dishonesty with The Major's image of absolute integrity. But what other conclusion could you come to?

I puzzled over it all through the flight back to Gatwick, and for most of the evening at the flat. I even woke up in the night thinking about it.

It was shortly after 10.30 am when I passed the Littleton sign. Mr Bombastic had jumped and worked adequately enough but he had done nothing to suggest, to me at least, that he was anything special. 'He was OK,' I'd reported to Paddy who grinned. 'He didn't impress you, you mean?'

'Well, yes.'

Paddy chuckled. "He's bone idle at home. Only does what he has to, so he does. But on the racecourse he's a different story, particularly after they've gone three miles – as you'll find out on Saturday.'

At least the ride took my mind off the present problem for a time. I was once again rehearsing what I was going to say as I slowed down approaching the thick hedge. Again I parked outside the front door which opened as I was about to ring the bell.

'Rod. Didn't expect to see you here today.' Charles, signs

of surprise lingering on his face, was in his usual away-from-the-racecourse uniform – leather-patched khaki jersey, cavalry twill trousers and suedes, with not a strand of his grey hair out of place.

'Something on my mind, Charles. Just passing this way on my way back from Paddy O'Reilly's. Thought I would call in.'

'Sure. Come into the office.' He led me into a smallish room to the right of the front door with a tall window looking out onto the drive. The whole of one wall was taken up with a bookcase stretching from floor to ceiling and packed with racing books. On the other walls were photographs of Charles, some soaring over fences, some of him on the receiving end of various presentations.

I took the armchair opposite the desk while he seated himself in the leather swivel chair on the other side of it, in front of a computer, copies of tomorrow's runners and several form books. 'Just got as far as Fontwell,' he said, pushing the books to one side.

'Charles, I went to interview the boss of *weRthebestbets.com* yesterday, a man called Michael Henderson.' Charles showed no sign of recognition. 'They are based in Jersey.'

'Good Lord. Odd place for a bookmaker.'

'Yes, that's what I thought. But he used to be a financier. Started *weRthebestbets.com* when Covid turned things quiet.'

I watched Charles's face closely. If anything was going through his mind, he was showing no sign of it.

'Anyway it grew rapidly, so much so that he took on a couple of young investment whizz kids and they want to go public, or rather place some of the shares. Hence the wish for an interview and publicity.'

Again no response. I breathed in, screwed up my courage and said a silent prayer. 'Charles, in the course of our talk, Michael Henderson said that he receives an email listing your tips each day at around 9.20am.'

This time there was a response. 'But they don't appear on the website until ten minutes later.' He looked puzzled, rather than worried. 'Do you think somebody in *sports-all. com* is sending them to him? I email the article and the tips to the office at 9.00am, or as near as dammit.'

I cursed myself. I hadn't thought of that possibility. I'd so nearly accused him - and made myself look a bloody fool into the bargain. Not to mention turning a friend into an enemy.

'If that is the case, then we have a Judas in the camp.' I desperately tried to regain the initiative. 'And he – or she – is in the pay of Hedgers because they also receive the tips, and they get them at about 9.10am.'

Charles picked up a plastic ruler from his desk, held it at each end and began flexing it as if to help him marshal his thoughts. 'OK,' he began slowly, leaning back in his chair and looking me straight in the eye, 'I'll tell you how it all happened.'

I said nothing, wondering what was coming. 'When Diana's cancer became worse in the last year of her life, I had to employ a nurse, part-time to begin with but then full time – and I had to have a second one, part-time, at weekends. This cost a lot of money, more than I could afford. I have a good deal with *sports-all.com* – but not that good.'

He was continuing to flex the ruler but now he was looking at it almost continuously. Only briefly did his eyes lift and catch mine. When they did, I began looking away. I was embarrassed, more so than Charles seemed to be. 'After Diana died, I found that I needed to continue to employ a nurse. Heather is paralysed from the waist down, as you know. There are often times, hygiene and others, when she needs help. I could see myself running out of money, and having to sell this place.' The ruler was almost bent double. 'Then salvation arrived, or so I thought. At the end of each month I found there was an extra £5,000 lodged into my bank account. There was nothing to say where it came from. To be honest, I didn't look too hard. I thought it was providence and, as we both know' – he smiled – 'you don't look a gift horse in the mouth, particularly in our business.

'Then one day at Sandown a man came up to me – a small but smartly-dressed man – and mentioned the £5,000. I tried to turn away but he grabbed my arm and said his firm was paying the piper and they demanded a tune in return. I was to send my tips to a certain email address at 9.00am each day. I refused point blank. Said I would go to the police if he didn't leave me alone.

'I thought I'd got rid of him but, when I got back from Worcester the following evening, I found Heather in tears. She said that two thugs had called to the house just after lunch, manhandled her and threatened her with a knife: 'Tell your daddy that we are going to carve a pattern on your face if he doesn't send us the tips.' They left a piece of paper with that email address on it.

'I couldn't risk Heather getting her face scarred. Not after all she's been through. I thought of instructing my bank not to accept the payments. But I needed the extra £5,000 so I began emailing the tips.' The ruler snapped. He tossed the two pieces into the wastepaper basket by his side.

'I did suppose that one day it might come out,' he said quietly. 'But I just tried not to think about that.' He learned forward in his chair and this time he did look me in the eye.

'I suppose you're going to put all this into your article.' Both his face and his voice were as dejected as a dog ticked off for chewing the carpet.

I shook my head. 'No. I don't need to,' I said slowly. 'Not at this stage. The article is about the company and what they're planning.

'But Charles,' I leaned forward to make sure he met my gaze. 'You do realise this is not going to last? There could be other interviews with other journalists, and the chances of Michael Henderson not mentioning any of this are slim. The odds against your involvement not coming out are...' I paused as I searched my mind for the right figure. 'Well, you can work it out better than I can. Let's say 10-1 against – at best. For those other journalists, it will be the story: "Champion tipster secretly sells his selections to bookmakers.'

I was deliberately laying it on thick, and turning the screw. I needed to make him realise what a mess he was in. For his sake, not mine.

He nodded.

'Charles, you've got to stop ... somehow... one way or another.'

'You're right. I do know that,' he said slowly. 'If I am exposed – and I fear I probably will be – the shame would be unbearable.' He glanced at the photographs on the wall.

My gaze followed his to the presentations and the one of him jumping the last at Sandown, presumably in the Grand Military Gold Cup. No throwing an arm out with him. He was as stylish as any professional.

'I did think of committing suicide if it happened.' His voice was now so normal he could have been discussing who would win at Cheltenham on Saturday. 'But I've got a lot of life insurance that Heather is going to need and they don't pay up if you kill yourself.'

I was horrified.

'Listen Rod,' He was now looking me straight in the eye. 'Will you give me a week? That will give me time for me to think things through, discuss everything with Heather and hopefully work out a plan for the future. To be honest, it doesn't really matter about me. I've had my life. It's Heather's life – or rather the rest of it, and her reputation, that I need to make arrangements for.'

I stood up. 'Of course. Charles, it's you I'm thinking of. You've been a big help to me, and I'm just sorry that my researches have uncovered this.'

He escorted me to the front door and, out in the hall, I felt Boris Johnson's eyes boring into me. He used to be a journalist. What would he have done?

Thursday, I was up at 6.00am to write the *weRthebestbets. com* piece after spending all the previous afternoon playing back the Michael Henderson interview and mapping the article. By 8.30am I'd checked it and filed it. I had other things on the schedule. Firstly a call to George Goodbody.

'George, Hedgers bookmakers,' I began. 'I know it's

a private company but I need to know who the main shareholders are, and any major changes in ownership in the last few months. I mean the real owners, not necessarily those officially listed. Can your man do this, and in a few days?'

'I'll ask him. Any rides coming up? He's sure to want to know.'

I hesitated. I'd feared this question was going to be asked. It was why I'd put off making the call when I came back from visiting Charles - and I still didn't know how to answer.

'George, I'm riding a horse called Mr Bombastic in the amateur chase at Cheltenham on Saturday. They're aiming him at the Festival in March, and I personally don't think he has much chance of winning on Saturday. But George, be careful what you say. I don't want the horse being backed off the boards because of this guy's screwed-up interpretation of what I tell you. The trainer certainly doesn't expect him to win on Saturday and, if he thinks I'm tipping people off, he won't put me up again.'

'OK, I get it.' George sounded vague, as if he was working out what to say to his unnamed punting-mad contact. 'I'll be careful how I phrase it.'

I suddenly had an idea. 'Give him a tip in another race. Hang on.' I hastily logged into the *Racing Post* site, found the main race and looked for Billy Black's mount. Humble Gratitude was a 6-1 chance. 'Tell him I believe Humble Gratitude has about four lengths in hand in the race before mine, but not to take less than 5-1. OK?'

'OK. Will it in win?'

'Yes.' I just hoped George wouldn't plunge. He might not

be so helpful in future if he went for a big punt and lost his money.

Over a delayed plate of cereal I checked my emails. The one from Brett I looked at first. 'Nice piece. On the website now. Any further developments on your Ludlow attacker? Could do with something on that for tomorrow morning.'

In other words: find something and get on with it. I was halfway through a cup of coffee when it came to me. I hadn't put the number in my phone but I went through the previous week's call history and, reckoning I'd found the right one, I dialled.

The Welsh accent told me I'd got it in one. 'Hi Dai,' I said cheerily. 'Rod Hutchinson here. Did you manage to get any further with finding those men that attacked me at Ludlow racecourse Monday last week?'

'Ah Mr Hutchinson.' The sing-song Welsh accent sounded friendly. I hoped it would also be helpful. 'We are continuing with our enquiries. Are you writing another article?'

'Yes – and I thought it would be good PR if I added a bit about what the police are doing. You know the sort of thing: we have a number of promising leads and we are hopeful they will lead us to the people responsible etc.'

'Aye, you can certainly say that. In fact we interviewed a suspect yesterday.'

'Oh. Can you say who? Was it the big thug that beat me up?

'No. This was a smaller man. No names but he gave us some very useful information. These men, as I think I told you, are wanted for a number of similar attacks. Yours is the only one on a racecourse, though. The others were in and around Birmingham. We are working closely with the C.I.D. in the area.'

'What about the bookmaker involvement in the case of my attack?'

'Aye. That was what I meant about useful information. Our suspect gave us a couple of names. Not of the bookie who paid for the job but of the go-betweens. When we catch up with them, we'll get the bookie.'

'That's great.' I had more than enough for my story – and I quickly brought the call to an end. I didn't want Dai telling me it was all off the record.

Things were going well. I decided to play my luck. I rang a local florist, gave them Emma's name, the surgery where she worked and asked them to deliver a dozen red roses sometime this morning. After giving my credit card details, I was asked what message I would like to send. 'Love you, Rod', would do fine I told the helpful lady at the other end.

POLICE CLOSE IN ON BOOKIE RESPONSIBLE FOR LUDLOW ATTACK was the headline that Brett put on my piece the following morning. I read it through – he hadn't changed a word – and gave myself a mental pat on the back, although it did little to cheer me up.

The florist had rung back late the previous afternoon to say that Miss Johnson had refused to accept the flowers. 'Should we try again, Mr Hutchinson? I've known that to work before now.' I could tell she was trying to turn an emotional disaster into something more hopeful. But clearly it was all over. I thanked her but said not to bother. I had another sleepless night.

I got out the form for Cheltenham Saturday and tried to concentrate on the Cleeve Hill Amateur Novices Chase. I hadn't got through more than a quarter of the field when my phone rang.

George Goodbody's name came up on the screen. My mood instantly changed from depression to excitement. He must have got somewhere to come back to me this quickly.

'Morning Rod,' he began cheerfully. 'My contact didn't take long, although he was short on detail. There is a certain James Brownson – real name could be something else – who has been buying up the Hedgers' shares in a series of private deals. Only a few are in his name but my man thinks he is behind the various pseudonyms, and that he now owns just over forty per cent of the company. I gave him the info about Mr Bombastic and told him to go carefully - said the one to be on in a big way is Humble Gratitude in the 3.00pm.'

'George, you're brilliant.' I felt like a man who had just been told he had won the Ascot jackpot. 'Thank you very much.'

James Brownson was no pseudonym. And Hedgers were in the frame.

15

Saturday dawned cold, grey and threatening with snow forecast to sweep in from the north-west during the evening. But I leapt out of bed – after a good night's sleep for once – like a spaniel going off to a shoot. Riding at Cheltenham. I could hardly wait.

There was only one vehicle in the car park - Cheltenham had a reserved area specifically for the racing press - and it was a far from new Toyota Corolla. I guessed it belonged to the white-coated attendant who strolled over, banging his gloves together to keep his hands warm, and said good morning as I took my wellingtons out of the boot before heading for the racecourse.

I'd walked the course at least once at every Festival meeting for the last three years, but this was different. I inspected the approach to each fence purely from a jockey's point of view: where I should be, where I should aim to take off and any possible problems on the landing side. I also looked at the big Cleeve Hill landmark from an altered perspective. It's looming mass appeared forbidding rather than interesting, and I could envisage it covered in snow. It was certainly cold enough, with an ominously icy wind almost as threatening as that big thug at Ludlow.

The third last fence was the one I particularly wanted to study, both from the approach and the landing side. It was on a downhill stretch and had an alarming tendency to separate the men from the boys - and the over-brave from their horses. It was taken at near maximum speed, and many horses proved unable to get their landing gear sorted in time.

I walked on, close to the white rails, as I headed towards the last two fences. Both were big, broad and stiff but relatively straightforward compared to the one I would meet coming down the hill.

Back in the now half-full press car park, warmed up and excited, I swapped the wellingtons for shoes, and my windproof for jacket and overcoat, took my laptop out of the boot and made for the press room. It was huge and barely a quarter full. So different from the Festival when every seat – all of them booked weeks in advance – was taken like the auditorium of a hit West End performance.

Charles was already there. Smart check suit, and camel-hair overcoat draped over a neighbouring chair. I put my laptop on the table one chair further along and nodded a silent greeting. 'Morning Rod,' he said getting to his feet. 'Got a minute?'

'Sure.'

'Not here. Let's take a walk.'

Putting on his coat, he said nothing further until we were in the empty parade ring. 'I've resigned from *sports-all.com* and this is my last day.'

'Good God.' I hadn't expected things to move this quickly, and I said as much.

'I went to see Brett yesterday,' he explained as we headed towards the parade ring exit to the chute that led out onto the racecourse proper. 'I told him that my eyes are not as good as they should be, and I have developed cataracts in both of them.' He smiled. 'This is true.'

'I said that studying the form for hours on end, day after day, was making them worse and I'd been advised to stop. I told Brett that I was therefore resigning from the end of the month. I have three weeks' holiday due and so I will do my last piece today.'

'God,' I repeated. Despite what I'd said on Wednesday, I hadn't expected anything like this. Nothing so abrupt anyway.

'In fact, I'd already paved the way for my replacement so Brett wouldn't feel he'd been completely left in the shit.'

'Oh. Who's that?' I asked as we got onto the racecourse and headed left towards the second last fence. The grass was damp, doing Charles's suede shoes no good. Mine were polished brown leather and better able to cope.

'Gerry Robson. He hasn't worked since The Clarion closed in March and he said he'd be delighted to replace me - assuming he was acceptable to Brett – and he was when I reminded Brett that Gerry had won the naps table award last year.'

'And will you be alright, Charles? Income-wise? '

Charles kept walking at the same pace but he took several seconds to answer. 'I'll manage,' he said slowly. 'A couple of the big stables have contacted me in the past about advising them on placing their horses, but I always said I couldn't because of my journalistic work. It wouldn't look right if I was receiving money from anyone else.'

I looked at him sharply. But the irony of what he had just said seemed to have escaped him. His serious expression remained.

'Now that I've retired, or will do after today, the situation is quite different. I'm going to speak to one or two of the big owners as well - those that might appreciate my services.'

We stopped between the last two fences. 'But Rod. I don't want anyone to know about this until Monday when my retirement announcement will appear on the website. I need Hedgers to be presented with a fait accompli. I don't want them getting wind of what I'm doing, and using strong-arm tactics against Heather to make me change my mind.'

I assured him that Monday's piece would be as big a surprise to me as it was going to be to the rest of the racing world.

'Thank you Rod.' We both turned and began the journey back through the wet grass. 'And thank you for not blowing the gaffe on the whole thing. At least I can bow out on my terms and with my reputation unscathed.'

As we reached the parade ring we were hailed by a familiar figure. 'Hello Charles. Hi Rod.' Arthur Jackson greeted us cheerily. I was glad to see that the Hedgers PR representative had no binoculars with him. He probably didn't have the ability to lip read but he might have been able to pick up something. Certainly he would recall me and Charles in deep conversation when he read the website on Monday morning.

The three of us chatted cheerily about the prospects for the big race, and briefly about Mr Bombastic's chances. 'He's a nice horse. Just the sort to go well in the National Hunt Chase in March,' said Arthur encouragingly and, looking up at the greying horizon to the north-west, he added: 'The forecast says the snow won't arrive until after the last.'

His cheerful manner was, as always, highly infectious. Whatever about others in Hedgers, I was convinced that Jackson was as clean as the driven snow - whose arrival everyone now seemed to regard as inevitable.

After retrieving my racing grip from the boot, and being shown to a peg in a corner of the large jockeys' room by Jim Simons - 'I've put all you amateurs together' - I returned to the press room, got out my list of questions and worked out which trainers should be available in which races. The famous King George VI Chase at Kempton on Boxing Day was now only two and a half weeks away,

Hilton winner Gallant George was the 3-1 favourite, despite having luck on his side at Sandown and being a few pounds worse off with most of the runners. John Barnard, standing outside the weighing room, was cautious: 'We gave him a week off after the Hilton and he's done well since, but this is level weights and the course is a bit sharp for a stamina horse like him. Shouldn't really be favourite but he'll run well.'

Mandable will be four pounds better with Gallant George for half a length, I pointed out to the red-faced Richard

Robson as he strode purposefully - saddle and weight cloth under his arm - from the weighing room towards the saddling boxes.

'Too true,' said the trainer, battered trilby in its unconventional back-of-the-head position. 'We'll get our revenge on him alright. Mine's in cracking form and I'll be very disappointed if we don't win this one.'

I just needed to get Oliver Chester-Beatty in a co-operative frame of mind and I would have the big three in the bag. I found him coming out of one of the boxes on the second floor of the grandstand.

'Hi Oliver,' I began in what I hoped was a confident, as well as a friendly-sounding, voice. He said nothing but at least he didn't try to ignore me. 'Just writing about the King George. How's Big Thomas been doing since the Hilton?'

The trainer looked at me without answering for what seemed like several seconds. 'Just stood in his box for days on end, unable to believe how unlucky he had been.' It was several more seconds before the ferret-face creased into a grin. I smiled in acknowledgement that my leg was being pulled.

'He's in great form and at Kempton lady luck is going to smile on us. If she doesn't, she'll have me to answer for.' I said nothing, willing him to say a bit more. He didn't, at least not until I presumed that the conversation was over.

The small man – he couldn't have been much more than five foot, four – grinned. 'You didn't ask me about Lazarus Luke.'

I hadn't dared. 'Oh.' I expressed surprise. 'How is he getting on.'

'Fully recovered. The vets originally said eight weeks' rest but the more I looked at his off-hind, and the more I felt it, the more convinced I became that it had healed. I got the vets in for a rescan and it was perfect. Just as important, the rest had done him good. He resumed work at the beginning of this week, and his enthusiasm was even better than it was before. I didn't let him do much but what he did had the pigeons flying. Assuming nothing else goes wrong, he'll be hard to beat in the Guineas – and you can quote me.'

I thanked him as I scribbled a few notes on my pad.

'And how are you getting on with finding out who paid those thugs to attack you at Ludlow?' he continued.

I told him what Detective-Sergeant Jones had said, plus rather more about my bookmaker suspicions than had appeared on the website - although I deliberately made no mention of Hedgers.

Chester-Beatty frowned. 'Be careful. Racing has an unfortunate knack of attracting crooks, and some of them are totally ruthless. Anybody that gets in their way is stamped on so hard they never recover.'

I thought of Heather - 'Tell your daddy that we are going to carve a pattern on your face' – and silently shivered.

Chester-Beatty put his hand on my right arm. 'Racing needs reporters like you Rod, reporters who tell it as it is. But take a bit of advice from someone who has been in this game a long time. A dead journalist is no good to anybody.'

With that he strode off along the corridor and down the next staircase. I shivered again.

I went back to the press room, silently resumed my seat and flipped through the *Racing Post* with Chester-Beatty's warning ringing in my ears. It was the second time in less than three weeks that I'd been advised to lay off – the third if I included the Ludlow thugs – and, like Charles on my first visit to his house, the trainer had indicated that I could end up dead.

I tried to concentrate on my search through the runners at the day's five racemeetings. I already knew that neither Bob Arrows nor Tom Swarter had anything at Cheltenham. Arrows had two at Chepstow, both ridden by Harry Jones, but Swarter had nothing anywhere. I'd now accepted in my mind that neither of the jigger twins had anything to do with Brown River's Bangor-on-Dee flop, and that their owner George Rickards was not involved with *weRthebestbets.com* in any way. But I still eyed all three with the gravest suspicion. And, while I tried not to admit it, they frightened me.

I got out my notes, switched on my laptop and tried to block out everything except the two news pieces I wanted to do before my ride on Mr Bombastic. Lazarus Luke was straightforward – the only check needed was the latest Guineas prices – but the King George VI piece required repeated references to the Hilton result. By the time I'd finished, and double-checked everything, there was only just over an hour to the Cleeve Hill Amateur Novices Chase.

I went outside to the bookmakers' line. I wanted to see what price Humble Gratitude was in the big race and I was surprised to see him out to 8-1. He'd been half that in the *Post*'s SP forecast. Seemingly George Goodbody's contact had taken no notice of my tip. Indeed he appeared to be working on his own 'all-are-crooks' theory. The favourite was as short as 6-4.

'What do you fancy Rod?' called out Jack Joseph while nephew Arnold, seated by the side of the odds board and looking cold despite a thick coat and scarf, gave me a silent nod in greeting.

'Dunno really, Jack. I thought maybe Humble Gratitude but he seems to have gone for a walk.'

'Yea, you can't give him away. The only one the punters want is the favourite. He's a ridiculous price for a 14-runner handicap chase like this.'

'Jack. What price is my mount in the next? Mr Bombastic.'

'8-1,' Arnold intervened in his pronounced Birmingham tones.

'We'll give you tens as it's you, Rod,' said his uncle.

I smilingly shook my head. 'Bad luck to back your own mounts. It is with me anyway. Something always goes wrong when I do that.'

'You reckon you've got a chance?' Arnold seemed suddenly to be taking an interest.

'Nice horse and I'm hoping he'll go well.' I was conscious of several punters closing to within earshot. 'But he lacks experience for this sort of company. Anyway, good to see you both again.' I turned on my heel and headed straight for the weighing room.

I made my way through the jockeys preparing to go out for the main race, nodded at Billy Black, Alec Smith, Robbie Bolton and a couple of the others, and reached my peg in the corner. Ben Walters was already there, pulling on his boots. He nodded a silent, but far from friendly, greeting.

I concentrated on putting on my racing jersey - Christopher

Mayhew's white with a red sash - and my white breeches. I'd got as far as slipping rubber bands above my wrists, to stop the sleeves filling with air, when Walters said: 'How's Emma Johnson?'

'Fine.' It was not a subject I wished to discuss, particularly with Walters.

'I heard on the grapevine that you two had split up.'

I didn't answer and, deliberately looking in the other direction, concentrated on the fit of my boots.

'Thought I'd ask her out,' said Walters as he picked up his saddle and headed for the trial scales.

I was furious. I knew that Walters was deliberately riling me, probably trying to get his own back for Exeter. I also knew that his ploy was working. For days, and worse still in the nights, I had tried not to think about Emma. I knew I had lost her, but my mind would not accept this as fact. Nor would my heart. I was still in love with her and the thought of her with a smarmy toad like Walters was unbearable.

I followed him to the trial scales, got Jim Simons to help me put the right amount of lead into the weight cloth, and joined the gathering around the largest of the various TV screens. 'Fuck. It's snowing,' said Walters. 'That's all we need.'

'It's only a few flakes in the wind,' said another of my opponents. 'Nothing much due for another hour at least.'

I hoped he was right. It didn't look good. If anything, the snow had increased by the time the runners came round for the first time. The favourite was four lengths clear and jumping like a stag. Humble Gratitude was well back, some twenty lengths behind the leader.

'They're going too fast,' said Walters.

'Balls,' countered the weather expert. 'He's different class.'

The favourite's lead was down to two lengths as he headed downhill towards the third last. He soared over the fence but crumpled on landing. Billy Black on Humble Gratitude was now fourth and quickening. At the final fence he was second and only two lengths off the leader. He got up in the last fifty yards, stood high in the irons and used his whip for a victory wave. My first thought was that Goodbody's man has learned a much-needed lesson. But I was more worried about the snow which was showing signs of beginning to come down in earnest.

I hurriedly weighed out and handed my saddle to Paddy O'Reilly. 'Jaysus. This fecking snow. If it doesn't ease up, I might have to wait for the January meeting to give Mr Bombastic his Cheltenham experience.'

'Ach, it's just a shower,' said one of the other trainers. 'I rang the forecast just now – said only snow showers till after 5.00pm.'

I glanced through the open door. The parade ring had only a sprinkling of white. Looked like the forecast might be right after all.

When I went out with the other nine riders ten minutes later it wasn't much worse, and the course itself looked largely green. Then it came again, this time in large flakes which settled on the grass. If nothing else, I was glad I'd put on my overcoat over my colours. Paddy O'Reilly, wearing the thicker of his two morning windcheaters, was stamping his feet to keep warm, and even the thick scarf that Christopher Mayhew had added to his camel-haired overcoat looked barely enough.

I noticed an official going from one group of trainer, jockey and owner to another and recognised it was Lawrence Matthews well before he reached us. 'The stewards have gone out to have a look at the course,' he said to Christopher, nodding in the direction of a landrover heading towards the back straight. 'We won't let the runners leave here until they come back.' Turning towards me, he said: 'That OK with you, Mister Hutchinson?' Was it just my accent, I wondered yet again?

But the result of the inspection was soon a foregone conclusion. The settling snow fast turned into a blizzard. Apart from the danger of the snow balling under the horses' hooves, there was the question of visibility – or rather lack of it. 'The rest of today's racemeeting has been abandoned,' announced the public address to the rapidly-dwindling crowd, most of whom were already heading for the car parks.

The sooner I got away the better. Driving in the dark in these conditions would be a nightmare. I changed as quickly as I could, went to the press room and emailed my two news stories. Most of the press corps had already gone and, as I put my laptop into its case only Tom Cameron, Charles and a couple of others were still typing away. I nodded a 'Bye, be seeing you' and hurried out to the car park.

It was almost dark and the snow was coming down harder than ever. There were only five cars in the press section, and no sign of the attendant. I was fumbling under my overcoat and into my jacket pocket for the keys when my phone rang. It was Brett. 'Rod, you know Charles is leaving us?'

'Yes, he told me but he asked me not to say anything to anyone until Monday when I gather you are going to announce it.' The light from the phone just about illuminated the driver's side of the car interior. Something didn't look quite right.

'Rod, you still there?'

'Sorry, yes. I'm in the car park and the snow is coming down in buckets.'

'Not to worry.' It was alright for him, he wasn't out in it feeling like Shackleton in the Antarctic. 'I've got Gerry Robson taking over the tipping but I wanted to warn you that I might need a bit more news than previously.'

'No problem, Brett. Glad to.' I glanced again at the inside of the car. There was something below the steering wheel.

When Brett rang off I switched on the torch of my phone and had a good look. There were four wires, two green and two yellow, hanging down from the box encasing the steering wheel column. I couldn't see where they led. But I'd seen enough.

I hurried back towards the press room and reached the door just as Charles was coming out. 'Charles,' I said breathlessly, and in a state of shock. 'I've got to find the police. There's a bomb in my car.'

Even in the poor light I could detect a glint in his eyes. "Let's have a look,' he said with unmistakeable enthusiasm.

'Charles, no. I'm serious. I've got to get the police.'

'OK, but let's make sure it is a bomb first. After two tours in Northern Ireland, I know a car bomb when I see one.'

I reluctantly put down my laptop case on the nearest table and followed him out into the swirling snow. The outside lights were on, as were those in the car parks, but the snow made everywhere much darker than it would normally have been at this time. There were still a few cars driving out, but in the area reserved for the press there were now only four left, including my BMW. Charles shone the torch of his phone through the driver's side window, and then went round to the passenger side to repeat the performance. He did the same with the front and rear windows. By now he was covered in snow.

'I don't think it's a bomb,' he said, none too confidently. 'The car manufacturers use green and yellow wires like these. In my experience bombers use black cables.'

His experience must have been at least twenty-five years ago. But I refrained from saying so. The situation was tense enough without me adding to it. And I could sense that Charles was on edge too.

'I'm going to look underneath,' he said, getting down onto his knees and then, moving awkwardly and slowly as if his joints were hurting, lying prone on his back in the snow on the driver's side. He inched himself slowly and uneasily sideways so that he was parallel with the car, and only inches away from it. He shone the torch under the car, from the front to the rear, and then back again.

'Nothing there,' he said, as he gingerly rolled clear and got to his feet, wincing as he did so. 'Not as agile as I used to be,' he grinned, brushing some of the snow and dirt off his coat. 'It must have been car thieves trying to hot-wire the ignition. These joy-riders have a soft spot for Beamers. It's not a bomb anyway.'

'But Charles,' I was scared, and I could tell it showed in my voice. 'Let's get the police – to be on the safe side. And anyway I'll have to report it for the insurance.'

'OK. Give me the keys and the remote. Let's open up and see what the damage is.'

I reluctantly fished them out of my pocket and handed them over.

'Stand back,' Charles commanded. I hastily retreated about five yards.

'No, further back. Get well away just in case.' Charles could have been back in the army, giving orders to one of his men. But I was disturbed by the sudden note of urgency in his voice - and I needed no second bidding.

I was twenty yards back when a blinding flash lit up the whole car park area and the racecourse entrance. Almost simultaneously there was a massive crumpf, so loud that I could feel the pain in my eardrums. The next thing I knew I was hit by an all-consuming blast of air that lifted me off my feet. It blew me backwards with a force so strong that I felt as if I was a sail in the midst of an ocean storm. I caught a glimpse of my beloved car enveloped in flames and of Charles, arms outstretched and his whole body in a ball of fire, being blown through the now-burning air towards me. I heard him scream, and the next thing I knew my body was agonisingly smashed into a brick wall.

16

The pain was worse than anything I'd experienced in a racecourse fall. And I was so dazed that I thought I must have passed out. My right ankle and my left elbow were hurting so badly I wished I had done. I lay there in agony for what seemed like an eternity, the slightest move sending jolts of unbearable torture though my whole body. It was as if I was being given an electric shock whenever I tried to shift position. But everything was hurting so much that I found it impossible to keep still. Even the electric jolts weren't enough to stop me trying to ease the agony. And every time I did so, I paid the excruciating penalty - and paid it with a vengeance.

Then I heard the sirens. I thought it was heaven, or hell, welcoming me into their fold. It was probably only ten minutes after the bomb went off but it felt like ten hours. A torch shone in my face.

'There's another one here,' shouted the torch shiner. 'And this one's still alive.'

Two more men, both in uniform, rushed up. Was I in the army, I wondered – with Charles as my commanding officer leading us all into a battle seemingly already lost?

'Don't move mate,' said one of the three. 'We're going to put you on a stretcher and take you into casualty.'

Just as I heard a vehicle approaching, I was blinded by light. 'Don't try to move,' said another. 'We'll be as gentle as we can.'

I felt two sets of hands lifting me - and the electric jolts returned just as agonisingly as before. I cried out as I was lifted off the ground sufficiently to have a stretcher slipped underneath me.

The transfer to the ambulance was almost pain-free by comparison. 'I'm Dr Morrison,' said a voice in my ear. 'Where does it hurt?'

'All fucking over,' I gasped unhelpfully, before pointing with my right hand to my left elbow and then to my right ankle. The doctor, who I later learned had been on duty at the racecourse, pressed a syringe into the ankle and then into the elbow, and almost immediately the pains eased. I slipped into a comfortable doze and marvelled at how pleasant life was.

When I came round I was lying on a trolley, wearing a blue hospital gown, and had a white-coated doctor on one side of me with a nice-looking nurse on the other. Was this what heavens is like, I wondered? I might be dead but I certainly wasn't in hell.

'Feeling more comfortable?' enquired the doctor who had

a Covid-style mask, but white, over his mouth and nose.

'Where am I?'

'Cheltenham General Hospital – and in the running for this year's luckiest man alive award.'

I wondered if I'd heard right at about the same time as I became aware of something big, solid and uncomfortable around my left elbow and another much the same encasing my right ankle.

'You fractured bones in your elbow and your ankle. I would imagine it happened when you hit the brick wall. There's also a fair bit of bruising on your back.'

I tried to recall what had happened, but I'd got no further than a horrific image of Charles encased in flames - and that scream - when I heard the doctor say something I couldn't quite catch about 'Not too bad. Didn't need to pin either of them.'

'So when will I be back in action?'

'They might want to keep you in for a day or so because, obviously, you were concussed,' replied the doctor. 'But, all being well, I don't see why you couldn't go home tomorrow or Monday.'

'No, I don't mean that.'

'I think he is talking about when he will be able to resume race-riding,' intervened the nurse who obviously knew more about racing than her medical colleague.

'Ah. That's quite a different matter,' said the doctor. 'Both plasters shouldn't need to be on for more than a month providing you are sensible and don't try to do too much. If you do, the bruising will swell and the plaster will have to be opened up and redone.'

I frowned as I tried to work out the dates. I'd need a month back in the saddle to convince Paddy O'Reilly and Christopher Mayhew that I was fit enough for Mr Bombastic in the National Hunt Chase. And, if he won in the meantime with somebody else in the saddle, that would put the kibosh on it. I had a painful vision of Ben Walters in the Mayhew white with red sash. And another of him with his arm around Emma.

'Listen,' said the doctor, obviously reading my air of dissatisfaction. 'You're bloody lucky to be here at all. Your colleague is in the mortuary and you could easily have ended up there too.'

That really hit home. 'Sorry,' I muttered. 'I was thinking about the Festival meeting in March, and whether I will be fit enough by then. But I guess that's not that important considering....' My voice tapered off as I thought of Charles. And Heather.

The door opened and a blue-overalled orderly cheerfully breezed in. 'Ah Harry,' said the doctor, his face breaking into a grin. 'Lester Piggott here is wondering why he can't be back riding next week. Maybe you can get through to him how lucky he's been, as you take the scenic route up to ward eleven.'

'Sure guv. My pleasure.'

Harry went round to the other end of the trolley, gripped the handle and we set off for the ward. There was no scenic route, just the lift, and it soon became apparent that the only luck he was concerned about was the bad luck of the favourite in the big race. 'Stupid bugger, that jockey. If he'd just gone a bit steadier going into that downhill fence, he'd have been alright. But what does he do? He kicks into it. Cost me twenty fucking quid.'

At the ward entrance he swivelled the trolley round, opened the swing doors with his backside and came a to a halt in front of the sister's desk. 'Mr 'Utchinson for you, Margaret,' he announced in a manner that suggested I was the prize she'd been waiting for all week, and disappeared back through the swing doors.

The sister picked up the clipboard at the end of the bed, studied it for a few seconds and said: 'Doesn't look as if you will be with us for very long, Mr Hutchinson. You could be out tomorrow. Monday at the latest.'

A small, middle-aged nurse came up and pushed me through a side door into a small room and was joined by another, much younger, nurse. Between the two of them, they lifted me onto the only bed in the room and disappeared.

As I lay there, propped into a semi-sitting position, I became aware that my back hurt. When I tried to ease the pain by rubbing it against the pillows behind me, it was a whole lot worse. I was also hungry. All I'd eaten since breakfast was a ham sandwich between the first two races.

When the younger nurse finally reappeared – it was probably only ten minutes but it felt more like half an hour – I told her about both problems.

'That's easily fixed,' she said, 'Here's your watch but I'm afraid your phone's had it.' She took both from a pocket in her uniform, showed me the phone's smashed face and put them in the drawer of the bedside table. 'Now let's have a look at that back.'

She helped me take off the hospital-issue pyjama top as I leaned forward to let her see the damage.

'Nasty,' she said as if she really meant it. 'I gather you were smashed against a brick wall by the blast. Just as well you didn't hit it face first.' She picked up a pot of what I presumed was some sort of cream from the bag at the bottom of the bed, and began rubbing it into the sorest parts. It hurt like hell but I said nothing. I knew it was doing me good and would help to ease the pain.

Five minutes later she was back with a plate of roast beef, boiled potatoes, carrots and cabbage. She pulled up the sliding tray towards me, declared 'enjoy' and was gone. I was so hungry I would have eaten anything – and it tasted fantastic.

I told her so when she reappeared twenty minutes later to show me how to use the single elbow crutch propped against the bed behind me. I found it unexpectedly easy to manage as I hobbled towards the bathroom.

When I returned and got back into bed, she handed me a glass of cloudy liquid. 'Take these,' she said, proffering two white tablets. 'They'll help you sleep.'

They certainly did. I was out in no time but when I woke up it was as if I'd been through it all again, only worse. This time it was me flying through the air in a ball of fire. Somehow I ended up on top of the main grandstand. Ben Walters, holding out a sort of trampoline for me to land on, shouted at me to jump and then whipped it away at the last minute. At the Festival meeting, when I was still in bed and paralysed, he won the National Hunt Chase on Mr Bombastic and announced in the TV interview that he was going to marry Emma.

I fished my watch out of the drawer. It was 6.15am. I hobbled to the bathroom and, when I came back, there was a cup of tea on the sliding tray. I eased myself back into bed, careful not to spill the tea, and lay back drinking it deep in thought.

I wondered about Charles. He'd been so keen to check out the car bomb. Was it the old soldier returning to a way of life he loved, back with the thrills and dangers of the near-wartime situation of Northern Ireland? Or had he seen a way of ending his problems without jeopardising Heather's life insurance pay-out?

Whatever the reason, his bravery had saved my life. And so had Brett's telephone call. Had he not rung when he did, I would have pressed the remote and been blown to kingdom come.

As I sipped the last of the tea, I resolved to start a fund in Charles's memory to raise the money Heather would need to set up her own equestrian centre. There were a lot of rich people in racing that I knew well enough to ask them to contribute.

And if other reporters were told by Michael Henderson about his receiving Charles's tips, I would write an article on what Charles had told me about Heather being threatened with a knife - and I would write it in such a way that Charles's good name would not be prejudiced in any way. I would describe the living nightmare of a father, having lost the woman he loved through cancer, being blackmailed as he tried to protect their only daughter from being mercilessly scarred for life.

I would also take Charles's advice about letting the racing authorities deal with Hedgers, or rather Jimmy Brownson. I would talk to John Jameson or, better still, go and see William Sommerville. He wouldn't hesitate to get the investigation ball rolling.

The police were bound to want to talk to me. But I'd be careful about what I said: better that the BHA do the inquiring than Detective-Sergeant Jones and his colleagues barging in to Hedgers, saying that I was accusing Jimmy of murdering Charles.

I would keep quiet about the jigger twins, at least for a short time. Not because I no longer thought they should be exposed. I still did, very much so. But I didn't want to hand over a big story like that to every other racing journalist in the country. It was going to be mine, and mine alone.

The lights came on in the main ward. I looked at my watch. It was 7.00am. The nurse of the night before came in to take my temperature. Presumably if you were in hospital you had your temperature taken, no matter what you were in for. Needless to say, it was normal.

She looked at the thermometer and wrote down the reading on the board at the end of the bed. She came back five minutes later carrying a laptop case. 'Mr Cameron brought this in yesterday evening, said it was yours. His car was damaged in the blast, his wife picked him up and they called in here on their way back home. He said he would return this morning to see you.'

Five minutes later she was back again. 'You've got a visitor.' I thought of Cameron eager to get his story. Or John Jameson, doing the bidding of his superiors. More likely, though, Detective-Sergeant Jones or the Cheltenham Police.

'She came last night when you were asleep. I told her to

come back before I go off duty at 8.00am.'

She? Could it be Belinda, perhaps – looking after her kid brother yet again? Or, more likely, Sarah? I was beginning to realise that the golden nugget of information she had overheard was Jimmy talking to Trevor.

Further speculation was halted by a voice I thought I would never hear again. 'Thank you, nurse.'

Emma, red jersey over those tight-fitting black trousers that turned me on so much, came rushing into the room. 'Oh Rod, darling,' she threw her arms wide. 'How will you ever forgive me? I've been such a selfish cow, thinking only of my own safety when you were taking on the villains of the racing world almost single-handed.'

Tears poured down her cheeks as she embraced me before kissing me passionately on the lips. She breathlessly explained how she had seen the Cheltenham bomb on the BBC news, listened to the report of the Major's death and of an unnamed amateur jockey being taken to hospital with serious injuries. She knew immediately it was me and, when my phone appeared to be switched off, she packed an overnight bag and got into her car. When she arrived in the ward and was told it was me, she burst into tears. The nurse took pity on her, booked her into a nearby B & B and told her to come back first thing in the morning. If I was allowed out today she would drive me home, she said. If it was tomorrow she would swap days off with Barbara. And, unless I didn't want her, she was going to stay in the flat for a couple of nights 'to make sure you can cope with all this.' She pointed to my plaster-cast covered elbow and gave my leg a squeeze just above the knee.

I assured her that I did want her – 'and I always will.'

Further responses were cut short by the return of the nurse who informed Emma that she would have to leave now as the daytime staff were due to arrive in five minutes. The doctors would be doing their rounds in an hour or so; if she came back at 11.00am Rod would know if he was allowed to leave today. Another passionate kiss followed, and Emma was gone.

I now knew that I wanted to marry Emma more than anything, even more than returning to the racing saddle. I decided I would ask her today, when she came back at 11.00am if I wasn't allowed out, or on the drive home if I was. I had, of course, her fist-punching father to contend with - but I was more worried about getting her to say yes before Ben Walters had a chance to muscle in. I was leaning back, delighting in the prospect, when the nurse returned pushing a phone on a trolley. 'You're in demand, Mr Hutchinson,' she said. 'It's your boss, and he says it's urgent.'

I picked up the receiver. 'Brett?'

'Rod. You OK?' It was the familiar greeting and, typically, he didn't wait for an answer. 'Listen. I've got Gerry Robson doing Charles's obituary. What I want from you is a full account of the bomb going off, how it happened, the damage it did, who you think was responsible, what the racing authorities must do now. Give it the full works. You got a laptop? Are you Ok to type?'

I assured him I would be fine. 'Good. Otherwise I was going to send Michelle. But much better you do it. And a whole lot quicker. Can you let me have the piece in, say, an hour from now?'

'Better make it two. To be on the safe side.' I probably could do it in one – there were no facts to check, no mapping. I had it all in my head. But I didn't want to feel under pressure.

'OK,' he agreed, with a distinct note of reluctance in his voice. 'But Rod. Don't talk to anybody until you see your piece on the website. Particularly not to any reporters. This is the biggest story we've had yet – and it's going on the front page.'

If it bleeds, it leads.